Y0-AFY-390

Exploring EARTH AND SPACE SCIENCE

5

GRA–LAS

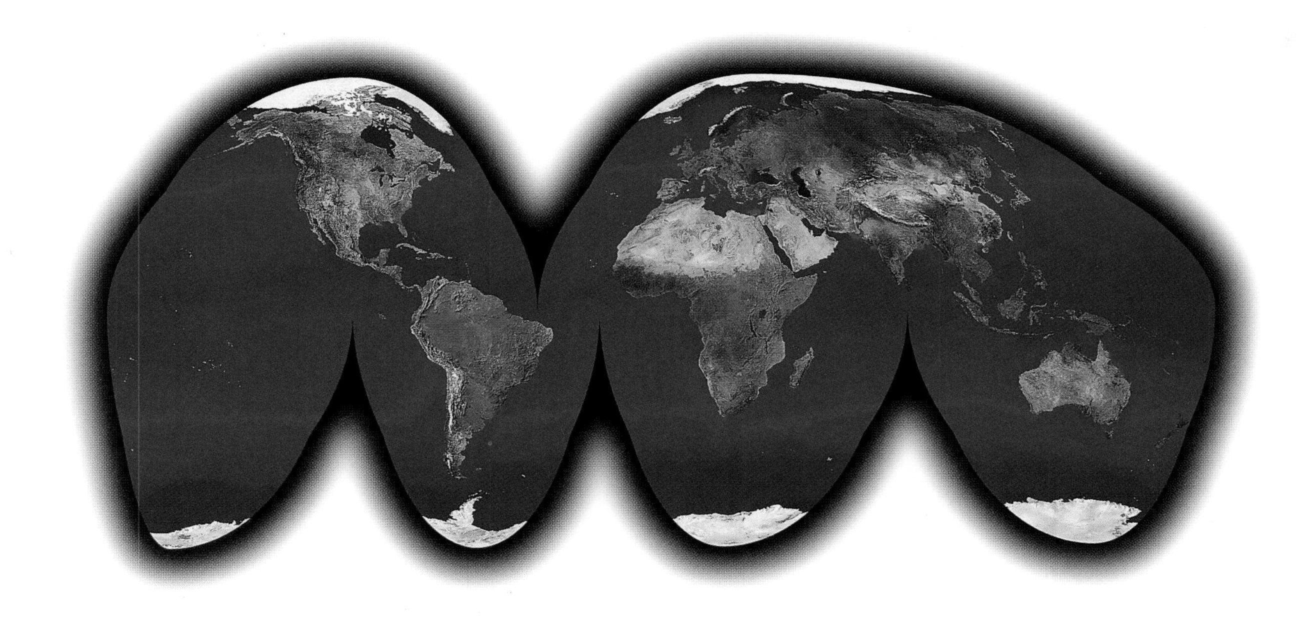

Marshall Cavendish
New York • London • Toronto • Sydney

Marshall Cavendish Corporation
99 White Plains Road
Tarrytown, New York 10591

Website: www.marshallcavendish.com

Created by **Brown Partworks Limited**

Library of Congress Cataloging-in-Publication Data

Exploring earth and space science.
p. cm.
Includes bibliographical references and indexes.
Contents: 1. Acid and base-Calcium -- 2. Calendar-Continental shelf -- 3. Copper-El Niño and La Niña -- 4. Energy-Gondwana -- 5. Grassland-Laser -- 6. Light-Meteor -- 7. Meteorology-Ordovician period -- 8. Ore-Prospecting -- 9. Protein-Star -- 10. Stratosphere-X ray -- 11. Index.
ISBN 0-7614-7219-3 (set) -- ISBN 0-7614-7220-7 (v. 1) -- ISBN 0-7614-7221-5 (v. 2) -- ISBN 0-7614-7222-3 (v. 3) -- ISBN 0-7614-7223-1 (v. 4) -- ISBN 0-7614-7224-X (v. 5) -- ISBN 0-7614-7225-8 (v. 6) -- ISBN 0-7614-7226-6 (v. 7) -- ISBN 0-7614-7227-4 (v. 8) -- ISBN 0-7614-7228-2 (v. 9) -- ISBN 0-7614-7229-0 (v. 10) -- ISBN 0-7614-7230-4 (v. 11)
1. Earth sciences--Encyclopedias. 2. Space sciences--Encyclopedias. 3. Astronomy--Encyclopedias

QE5 .E96 2002
550'.3--dc21 00-065801
CIP
AC

ISBN 0-7614-7219-3 (set)
ISBN 0-7614-7224-X (vol. 5)

Printed in Hong Kong

06 05 04 03 02 01 00 5 4 3 2 1

PHOTOGRAPHIC CREDITS

Corbis: Yann Arthus-Bertrand *393*, David Muench *331*, Staffen Widstrand *362–63*
Image Bank: Steve Allen *329*, Rokeach Aerial *356*, Sieplinga HMS Images *344*
NASA: *328*, *388–89*, Dryden Flight Research *346*
NOAA: *350*, *351*, Mr Ben Mieremet *380–81*, US Department of Agriculture *341*
Oxford Scientific Films: Ken Smith Laboratory @ Scripps Institute of Oceanography *358*
Robert Hunt: *386*, *336*
Science Photo Library: *340*, *354*, *364*, *385*, George Bernard *361*, BP/NRSC *372–73*, Chris Butler *391*, Jegou Christian *390*, CNES, 1995 Distribution SPOT Images *370*, Dr. Gene Feldman NASA *368–69*, David Ducros *355*, Mehau Kulyk *343*, Lawrence Livermore *396*, NASA *376*, NOAA *334*, Claude Nuridsany & Marie Perennou *335*, Prof. K. Seddon and Dr. T. Evans *382*, *383*, Rosenfeld Images Ltd. *378*, Bill Sanderson *326*, Fraser Simon *384*, Sinclair Stammers *333*, Tek Image *337*, Sheila Terry *374*, Dr. Arthur Tucker *338*, Erik Viktor *398*, Worldsat International *392*
TRH Pictures: United Nations *352–53*
Trip: I. Genut *342*, S. Grant *367*, W. Jacobs *348–49*, M. Jelliffe *366*, P. Joynson-Hicks *324–25*, Streano/Havens *332*, Th-Foto Werbung *360*, A. Tovy *395*, N. & J. Wiseman *394*

Front cover: Satellite image of the Gulf Stream around Florida (Science Photo Library, NOAA)

Title page: Projection of Earth's land and oceans (Science Photo Library, Worldsat International and J. Knighton)

Back cover: The Apollo lunar module (Marshall Cavendish)

Exploring EARTH AND SPACE SCIENCE

5

GRA–LAS

Marshall Cavendish
New York • London • Toronto • Sydney

Grassland

Large area where the ground is covered by grass and grasslike plants

The great prairies of the American West are an example of a biome (major life zone with a distinct climate) called a grassland. Grasslands are places where the ground is covered by a variety of grasses or grasslike plants.

There are many different types of grasslands, and all occur in fairly windy regions that have a moderate rainfall—between 10 and 30 inches (25 to 76 cm) each year. In the tropics, some grasslands are wetter than this, receiving more than 50 inches (127 cm) of rain in a wet season, which alternates with a long dry season. In grasslands, enough rain falls to support the growth of grasses but not enough for trees.

The world's grasslands

The world's largest grasslands are found in regions that lie between hot deserts and tropical or temperate forests. Almost all grasslands are found on plains or in rolling hills in inland areas. Grasslands are found up to 16,000 feet (4,877 m) above sea level.

HIGHLIGHTS

- Grasslands are large areas covered mainly by grass. They support a variety of species of grazing animals and meat-eaters.
- Climate greatly influences where grasslands are found and the type of grasses that grow there. The world's largest grasslands occur in areas lying between deserts and forests.
- Many of the world's main grain-growing regions are in areas that were once grasslands.
- Grassland soil is high in rich humus, which contains nutrients that fertilize plants.

About 13 million square miles (34 million sq km) of Earth's surface, which is about a quarter of all the dry land, is classed as grassland. As well as the vast U.S. prairie, large grasslands are also found in Eastern Europe, Russia, and South America. An immense area of grass covers much of south and central Africa. The African grasslands are home to lions and herds of zebras, elephants, antelope, and gazelles.

Grasslands are called different names in various parts of the world. In central Africa they are called savannas. South African grasslands are called the veld. In Russia, they are called steppes. In South America, they are called pampas.

Climate and vegetation

Climate is the main factor that determines where grasslands are found and also the types of grasses that grow. There are about 7,500 species of grasses. However, the number of different plant species that grow in any one grassland is fairly small, ranging from as few as 50 species to as many as 350 species.

In regions close to deserts—where temperatures are high and rainfall is low—short, scant grasses mingle with shrubs. These short

Tall grasses in the African savanna at the height of the dry season, when the flowerheads have turned over to seeds.

grasses, called savanna grass, grow in clumps and do not cover the whole ground surface. On the vast African savannas where these grasses grow, solitary trees such as baobab, acacias, or palms dot the open plain here and there.

In temperate regions farther from the equator (ih-KWAY-tuhr; imaginary line around Earth at equal distances from the North and South Poles), tall buffalo grasses such as bluestem and prairie cordgrass are common. Thistles, tumbleweed, and sunflowers also grow. These plants have tough and leathery leaves that are covered with bristly hairs, which put off grazing animals that might eat them.

Grasses die back each year, which means that a large amount of plant matter is added to the soil. Plant matter and also the bodies of dead animals rot, forming a rich layer called humus (HYOO-muhs), which helps new plant growth. Grassland soil contains up to 20 percent humus—five to ten times more than forest soil. This rich surface layer helps to prevent nourishing minerals from being washed to deeper levels by heavy rain, in a process called leaching. Because of their rich soil, grasslands are good for growing crops. Most of the world's grain crops are grown on land that was once grassland. Grasslands are also used for grazing domestic livestock.

Fires quite often break out in grasslands because of the hot, dry conditions. Many fires are now started by people; in earlier times, they were usually started by lightning. Surprisingly, fire is good for grasslands. It kills large shrubs, such as mesquite, which tend to take most of the nutrients (goodness) in the soil.

Grassland life

Grasslands support a wide variety of creatures, which in turn help the plants to flourish. Huge numbers of microscopic life-forms, including bacteria (single-celled organisms), fungi (FUHN-JY; organisms that lack chlorophyll), algae (AL-jee; plantlike organisms), and viruses (VY-ruh-suhz; tiny infectious agents), live in the soil. A variety of larger creatures also thrive both below and above ground. Animals of the grasslands fall into two major groups: burrowers that take shelter from predators below ground, and grazers and meat-eaters that live above ground.

In the United States, grazers such as mule deer, pronghorn, antelope, and jackrabbits share the plains with burrowing creatures such as ground squirrels and prairie dogs. Large numbers of insects also thrive in grasslands. In the short-grass prairie of Colorado, for example, more than 1,600 insect species have been found. Birds also inhabit grasslands, but the scarcity of water limits their numbers and species. Bird life in the United States's grasslands includes prairie chickens, burrowing owls, and many hawks.

CHECK THESE OUT!

✔AFRICA ✔CLIMATE ✔NORTH AMERICA ✔RAIN, SLEET, AND SNOW ✔SEASON ✔SOUTH AMERICA

Gravity

The force of attraction between all objects in the Universe

One of the most famous scientific legends of all time states that English scientist Sir Isaac Newton (1642–1727) got his key insight into the nature of gravitation when he chanced to observe an apple falling to the ground. Gravity, however, is not just a force that pulls objects toward Earth: it pulls any two objects toward each other. Gravity explains why things do not fall off Earth as it spins around, why the planets circle around the Sun in regular orbits, and why astronauts weigh less on the Moon than they do on Earth.

English scientist Sir Isaac Newton discovered the law of universal gravitation.

The history of gravity

No one knows whether Newton's apple actually existed, but scientists know that Newton was not the first to consider the mysteries of gravity. Ancient Greek philosopher Aristotle (384–322 B.C.E.) was probably the first person to investigate gravity. He wrongly concluded that gravity makes heavy objects fall faster than light ones. Around 1589, Italian physicist Galileo Galilei (1564–1642) found that all falling objects accelerate toward Earth at the same rate, no matter how heavy or light they are. A feather falls more slowly than a rock because air resistance slows it down more. Without air, feathers and rocks would fall at the same speed.

Danish astronomer Tycho Brahe (1546–1601) and German astronomer Johannes Kepler (1571–1630) studied how gravity makes the planets move around the Sun. Kepler worked out that planets move in oval orbits called ellipses (ih-LIP-SEEZ). He demonstrated that planets move faster when they are closer to the Sun, and that the time they take to travel once around the orbit (called the period) also depends on their distance from the Sun.

In 1687, Newton combined the findings of Galileo, Brahe, and Kepler into a single mathematical theory called the universal law of gravitation. This law shows that any two objects attract one another with a force that depends

HIGHLIGHTS

- Isaac Newton produced the first universally applicable law of gravitation in 1687.
- Gravity obeys Newton's law of action and reaction. Falling objects pull Earth upward with as strong a force as Earth pulls them downward.
- When large masses are involved or when objects move at speeds close to the speed of light, Einstein's general theory of relativity gives more accurate results than Newton's law.
- Einstein's general theory of relativity was a more complex account of gravity than Newton's law of gravitation.

both on the masses of the objects and the square of the distance (the distance times the distance) between them. The heavier the masses, the greater the force. In addition, the greater the distance between the masses, the less the force.

Newton's law of gravitation is related to his laws of motion, which explain what happens to objects when forces act on them. His first law of motion says that objects stay still or travel in straight lines unless forces act on them. Thus, because planets move along ellipses, some sort of force must be acting on them. Newton also said that when a force acts on an object, there is an equal and opposite force (called a reaction) that acts the other way. Gravity is therefore a two-way force; a falling apple is not simply pulled down by Earth, it also pulls Earth up toward it with an equal force. Earth is much more massive than the apple, so the apple's effect on Earth is unnoticed.

LOOK CLOSER

Black Holes

A star is mostly burning gas that is undergoing nuclear fusion (where small atoms are joined to make larger ones). When the fusion process has gone as far as it can, the star collapses in on itself. Neutron stars are produced in this way. When very massive stars collapse, the result is called a black hole.

According to Einstein's theory of gravitation, the huge amount of mass in a black hole produces so much curvature in nearby space that nothing can escape from it. Since even light is trapped inside the star, a black hole can only be seen through the effect it has on the motion of material or stars nearby.

Mass and weight

In everyday language, the terms *mass* and *weight* are often used to mean the same thing. The idea of gravity helps to explain a very important difference between them. Mass is a measure of how much of something there is. Weight is the force on a mass when another mass is nearby. For example, mass is a measure of how much material (mainly water) makes up someone's body. Weight is a measure of how much that person is attracted to Earth by gravity; their weight depends on their mass. Their mass stays the same no matter where they go in the Universe. Their weight, however, varies from place to place depending on nearby objects. If that person went to the Moon, they would have the same mass but they would weigh much less because the Moon's mass is about one-hundredth that of Earth. A much smaller force of attraction between their body and the Moon is therefore produced.

When an object is thrown horizontally, gravity makes it follow a curved path toward Earth (a). If the object is thrown at increased velocity, it will travel farther before hitting Earth (b and c), until a velocity is reached at which the object will not fall to Earth (d). The object is then in orbit.

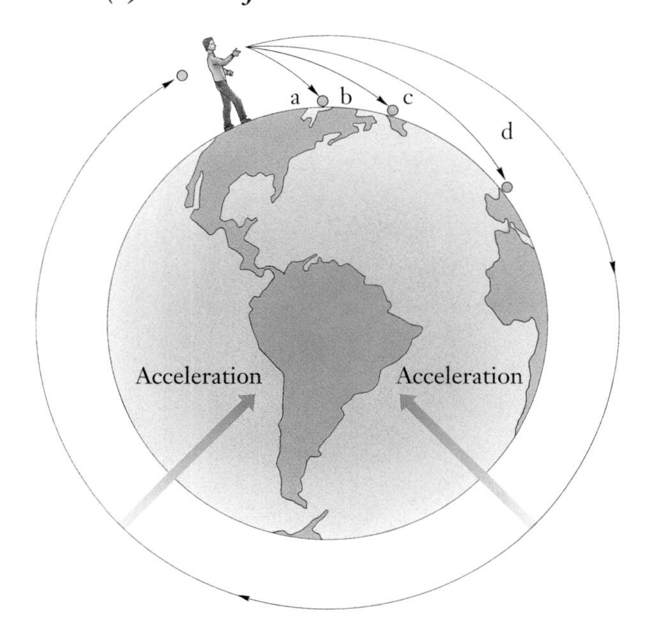

Acceleration due to gravity

According to Newton's laws of motion, when a force acts on an object, it makes the object accelerate (move more quickly), and the bigger the force, the greater the acceleration. The force of gravity also makes objects accelerate. This fact explains why skydivers travel faster and faster after jumping from an airplane. As Galileo found, all falling objects accelerate at about the same rate. It is only air resistance that makes a parachutist fall to Earth more slowly than a skydiver; gravity pulls them down with exactly the same force. Although the acceleration due to gravity, as this is called, is about the same all over

Gravity draws objects toward Earth's surface. It is also responsible for holding the Moon in orbit around Earth.

Earth, it varies slightly because Earth is not a perfect sphere. Acceleration due to gravity is therefore a little greater at sea level than at the top of Mount Everest; when something is farther from the center of Earth, the force of gravity is slightly weaker.

Gravity in space

Newton's law of gravitation works well most of the time but not with massive objects or with objects that are traveling close to the speed of light. German-born U.S. physicist Albert Einstein (1879–1955) developed Newton's ideas into a more complex account of gravity called the general theory of relativity.

One of the theory's central ideas is that acceleration due to gravity is the same as any other acceleration. If a ball dropped inside a space rocket falls toward the floor, there could be two possible explanations. First, the rocket might be on Earth, in which case the ball would be pulled to the floor as objects normally are on Earth. Second, the rocket might be accelerating into space, so the floor of the rocket would move toward the ball while the ball stayed still. The effect would be the same in each case. This idea that gravity is the same as acceleration is called the principle of equivalence (ih-KWIV-uh-luhnts).

Einstein's theory also suggests that gravity is not a mysterious force acting on objects from a distance. Instead, gravity is a curvature (bending) of space and time near any mass or energy. This curvature makes the path of a moving object bend unexpectedly in the same way as if a force (gravity) were acting on it.

Einstein's theory of gravitation explains many unusual events. It explains why starlight bends as it passes by the Sun during an eclipse, and it also explains why Mercury's orbit differs very slightly from an ellipse.

EVERYDAY SCIENCE

Artificial Gravity

Astronauts train in artificial gravity machines to prepare for the high gravitational forces (g-forces) encountered during rocket launches. They sit in a cockpit at one end of a long metal arm, which is spun around very quickly by a powerful motor. This spinning creates a force rather like that created by amusement-park rides. The faster the wheel spins, the greater the g-force produced.

The same idea may one day be used to create space stations that have an artificial gravity similar to that on Earth. These stations could be massive, slowly rotating structures rather like bicycle wheels. People would live inside the "tire" of the wheel, and the speed of rotation could be adjusted to produce an outward force that felt like gravity on Earth.

CHECK THESE OUT!

✔FORCE ✔MASS ✔MOON
✔NEWTONIAN PHYSICS ✔RELATIVITY ✔SPACE

Groundwater

The world's store of water that is found under the ground

HIGHLIGHTS 

- There is about one hundred times more water under the ground than there is in all the lakes and rivers of the world.
- Water collects in sediments and porous rock, above nonporous rock such as clay. The zones in which the water collects are called aquifers.
- The water table is the surface at and below which there is groundwater.
- Groundwater reaches the surface in a number of ways: as springs, marshes, lakes, desert oases, and geysers. Water can also be raised by people through wells.
- Too much groundwater is being raised in many areas, and the water table is falling.
- Groundwater has created huge caverns under Earth's surface. Stalactites and stalagmites later formed—and are still forming—in the open spaces in underground rocks.

People on Earth often call Mars the red planet. If there were people on Mars, they would probably call Earth the blue planet because nearly three-quarters of Earth's surface is water. From space, the blue of the oceans is visible long after the landmasses are too small to see. Even on dry land, water in the lakes and rivers is an important feature almost everywhere.

There is about one hundred times more water underground than in all the lakes and rivers of the world. The volume of this groundwater is calculated at 2.4 million cubic miles (10 million cu km). Even beneath the dry sands of the Sahara Desert, there is as much as 150,000 cubic miles (625,000 cu km) of water.

Earth is the only planet in the Solar System where water occurs in all three forms: as a solid, as a liquid, and as a gas. Water moves through a never-ending cycle. Liquid water changes into its gaseous form (water vapor) by evaporation or by being transpired (given off) by plants from their leaf surfaces. The water vapor condenses in the atmosphere as clouds and falls back to Earth's surface as rain, snow, or hail. Once on Earth, the water can freeze into sheets of solid ice.

This lake is a body of groundwater that has come to the surface. Most lake water is cold, but this one is hot, as it has been heated by the rocks below.

Some of the rain and the water from melting ice and snow sinks deep into the ground to become groundwater. Part of this groundwater may have fallen to Earth tens of thousands of years ago. Millions of years ago, more water was buried as Earth's surface changed. Some groundwater dates from the time when Earth first began to form out of a cosmic dust cloud.

As surface water sinks down, it passes through several porous (POR-uhs; that liquids can travel through) layers. For a short distance below the surface, there is a layer containing both air and water. This layer is called the unsaturated or aeration zone. Lower down, every crack and pore is filled with water. This area is called the

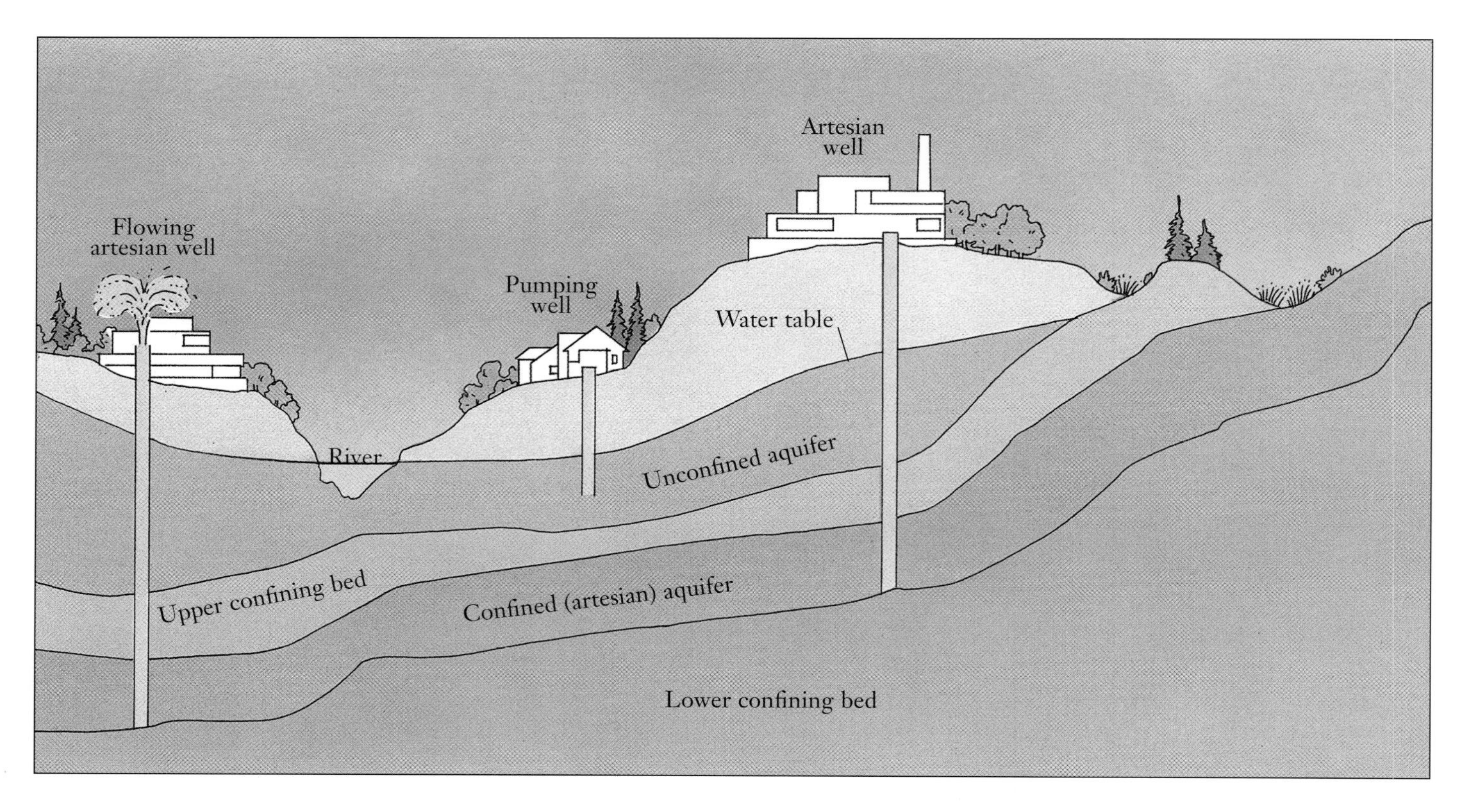

Groundwater can be pumped up from unconfined aquifers, or it can be pushed up under its own pressure from a confined (artesian) aquifer.

saturated zone. There is no definite boundary between these two zones, but the top of the saturation zone is called the water table. The distance down to the water table can change from season to season and day to day. If more water is taken (for domestic, agricultural, or industrial use) than is seeping down from the surface, the level of the water table drops.

Groundwater does not usually move in big underground rivers and streams. Rather, it moves through the pores and cracks of solid ground. Surface water from rain or melting snow sinks down through porous rocks like sandstone and limestone and then reaches an impermeable (im-PUHR-mee-uh-buhl; not allowing liquids to pass through) layer of material, such as clay or another nonporous rock. The water then collects there as groundwater.

The layers where groundwater collects are called aquifers, from the Latin word meaning "water carriers." Water moves along an aquifer to an outlet, such as a spring, or remains stored underground. Aquifers can form one below the other, separated by impermeable layers. The uppermost aquifer has no impermeable layer above it, and so it is called unconfined. Lower aquifers are confined between two impermeable layers, and because of this the water in the aquifer can be under quite a lot of pressure.

Although water in the open is always horizontal, the level of the water table roughly follows the contours of the ground because groundwater moves rather like that in a household plumbing system. Because the water is under pressure, it can be forced through pores and cracks in the rock, just as in the home, water under pressure flows through pipes into the taps.

Groundwater comes to the surface

Where Earth's surface comes below the water table, groundwater breaks out. It can be in the form of a spring, a marsh, a lake, or a desert oasis (a fertile area in a dry region). Springs can also form where a confined aquifer is under pressure and a fault in the rock gives access to the surface.

In some places, groundwater can be heated by volcanic material in Earth's depths. Pressure builds up until some of the water turns to steam.

The water and steam erupt to the surface as a geyser (hot spring). A good example is Old Faithful, a geyser in Yellowstone National Park, Wyoming. This geyser is so named because it continues to erupt at regular intervals that can be predicted.

Groundwater can also be heated by the normal increase in temperature that occurs below Earth's surface. Every 300 feet (100 m) below the surface, the temperature increases by some 1.8°F (1°C). If a confined aquifer runs deep enough, it will be heated so that the pressure increases sufficiently to force it to the surface. At Warm Springs, Georgia, the groundwater descends to 3,000 feet (900 m). There it is forced to the surface at a temperature of 88°F (31°C).

For many thousands of years, humans have found ways to get at groundwater. This was first done in the Middle East, where wells were dug long before mechanized digging equipment was invented. The wells reached considerable depths, and water had to be hauled to the surface in buckets attached to ropes. Today, the water from most wells is pumped to the surface.

If a well goes deep enough to reach a confined aquifer, the pressure can force the water to escape upward, sometimes with great force. Wells of this kind are called artesian (ahr-TEE-zhuhn) wells. They take their name from the Artois region of France, where they were first studied. The world's largest artesian aquifer system is Australia's Great Artesian Basin. It lies beneath

LOOK CLOSER

Carlsbad Caverns

Beneath the ground of southeast New Mexico lies one of the natural wonders of North America. Carlsbad Caverns National Park includes probably the best-known of the groundwater-sculpted limestone caverns in the United States. The Carlsbad rocks were formed hundreds of millions of years ago, in the Upper Paleozoic era. At that time, the area was part of the vast North American inland sea. A reef formed, where organisms containing calcium lived and died, their remains gradually hardening into limestone. As millions of years passed, the bed of the sea rose and the limestone reef was buried below the water table.

Limestone, which is a form of calcium carbonate similar to chalk, does not dissolve in pure water. However, surface water will absorb carbon dioxide from the air, forming dilute carbonic acid. This reacts with limestone to form calcium bicarbonate, which is water soluble (capable of being dissolved in water). This is how the Carlsbad caverns were formed.

Over tens of millions of years, acid groundwater dissolved great cavities through the Carlsbad reef. Then, during the last million years, the water table dropped below the level of the caverns. Groundwater continued to drip down into the open spaces. Slowly, some of the dissolved calcium bicarbonate gave up its carbon dioxide, leaving behind another form of calcium carbonate called calcite. This material formed long icicle-shaped stalactites (stuh-LAK-TYTS) hanging from the cavern ceilings, and stalagmites (stuh-LAG-MYTS) building up from the floor below. Where the two met, they formed columns of calcite. The process is still going on.

Water slowly flowing down the walls of the caverns has built up as flowstone, a carbonate material that looks like sheets of ice. Tiny amounts of other minerals in the water have created a rainbow of colors within the rock.

676,000 square miles (1,750,000 sq km) of farmland. Artesian water often comes from ancient seas that were submerged (pushed under) during the formation of Earth's surface. This is the case in the Great Artesian Basin, and the water is therefore too salty for agricultural use. The water is fit for cattle to drink, however, as they need a certain amount of salt.

Water for the future

Groundwater from springs and wells provides 60 percent of the world's drinking water. The world's water consumption is now more than 1,030 cubic miles (4,300 cu km) each year. In the United States, more than 75 percent of all cities use groundwater for part of their domestic water supply, and 95 percent of rural homes use well water. In Canada, groundwater is some 10 percent of the water consumed, but it is the only source for 25 percent of homes.

The population of the world is increasing constantly and it has been estimated that it will double in the next 50 years. Conservation of water supplies is becoming one of today's most important problems.

Individual people in industrialized countries already use much more water than they used to, since most houses have running water. This has

Wheat being harvested in a huge field in the Great Plains. The enormous volume of crops grown need large amounts of irrigation water.

EVERYDAY SCIENCE

Groundwater in the Great Plains

The Great Plains, covering the states of Colorado, Kansas, Nebraska, New Mexico, Oklahoma, South Dakota, Texas, and Wyoming, are part of the breadbasket of the world, producing more than $20 billion worth of crops a year. Around 20 percent of the world's irrigation water (water used on land by means of ditches or artificial channels) comes from underground sources. Between 1940 and 1980, U.S. farmers pumped 120 cubic miles (500 cu km) of water onto the Great Plains to irrigate them.

The main source of this water is the Ogallala aquifer, the largest in the world. It contains 80 percent of the groundwater that is beneath 174,000 square miles (450,660 sq km) of the Great Plains. The water in the Ogallala aquifer would cover 3.2 billion acres (1.3 billion ha) to a depth of 1 foot (30 cm), each acre holding 389,474 gallons (1.48 million l). Some 170,000 wells pump water for corn, wheat, soybeans, cotton, and livestock.

The rocks of the Ogallala aquifer are probably no older than between 5 and 18 million years, and probably less than 10 million years. During that time, hundreds of feet of sediment—sand and gravel—were deposited in rivers and their floodplains, forming a thick porous layer. During the last ice age, water from the melting glaciers that covered the Rocky Mountains flowed east and filled the sediment with water. This is the water that fills the Ogallala aquifer. The sandy gravel beds are 50 to 300 feet (15 to 90 m) below the surface, and 150 to 300 feet (45 to 90 m) thick.

If it was emptied, the Ogallala aquifer would take 6,000 years to refill. Today, the water from melting snow in the Rockies flows south in the Pecos River and the Rio Grande, and the Ogallala aquifer receives only about 1 inch (2.5 cm) of water each year. At the same time, some wells in the region lower the water table by 5 feet (1.5 m) every year. It has been calculated that water that once cost $15 per acre must now be taken from the Missouri and Mississippi Rivers at a much greater cost of $800 per acre.

An oasis occurs where groundwater comes to the surface in a desert. Oases are very valuable to all desert life from plants to animals, including people.

led to concerns about the overuse of groundwater. Industrial demands as well as domestic supplies and agriculture are lowering the water table in many areas. In coastal regions, taking too much fresh water from wells allows salt water from the ocean to seep in and make the well water salty. At the same time, surface water systems can be affected by the lowering of the water table and damaged by salt.

Taking away more groundwater than can be replaced from the surface can also cause subsidence (suhb-SY-duhns; settling down of soil). Bangkok, the capital city of Thailand, is sinking at a rate of about 5 inches (12.5 cm) each year because the groundwater beneath the city is being used up so rapidly.

Another serious problem is the pollution of groundwater. The soil, sand, gravel, and porous rock above the water table filter out most dangerous bacteria and other infective organisms, as well as many chemical substances. However, some polluting substances still get through to the aquifers, and the number of polluting substances that people are producing is increasing all the time. Major sources of pollution include septic tanks, landfills, pesticides, fertilizers, and industrial waste. Even the salt used to clear ice and snow from roads and the accidental spillage of petroleum products can be very dangerous.

The contamination of groundwater is a very difficult problem to solve. The source of the groundwater may be far away from the areas in which it is used. The source must be identified and protected from contamination. Once groundwater is contaminated, cleaning it up can be expensive and time-consuming. This is sometimes impossible using current technology.

CHECK THESE OUT!
✔GEYSER ✔HYDROLOGY ✔RIVER ✔WETLAND

Gulf Stream

The strong current in the western North Atlantic Ocean

The powerful, warm current in the North Atlantic Ocean is called the Gulf Stream. This is one of the world's best-known ocean currents. It flows northeast from the southeast coast of the United States, past the Grand Banks of Newfoundland, and out across the Atlantic. As the North Atlantic current, it warms the shores of northern Europe, making the climate there much milder than in Newfoundland, which lies as far north. The Gulf Stream shifts more water than a thousand Mississippi Rivers.

The Gulf Stream is part of the generally clockwise flow of water in the North Atlantic. The flow is influenced by Earth's rotation. As in other oceans, the North Atlantic's strongest current—the Gulf Stream—flows along the west. It begins as the Florida Current in the Gulf of Mexico. This warm current then surges through the narrow passage between Florida and Cuba. It follows the coastline of the United States northeastward, moving at a surface speed of 3 to 4 knots per second, and is about 60 miles (100 km) wide. At Cape Hatteras off North Carolina, the coastline curves back northwest. The Gulf Stream continues northeast and shoots out into the open ocean. Between Cape Hatteras and the Grand Banks, it reaches its maximum strength and develops large meanders (loops). The current is strongest near the surface.

Warm waters

The swift waters of the Gulf Stream form a boundary between the warm Sargasso Sea east of Florida and the cold waters off the coast of Newfoundland to the north. Ocean temperatures off Newfoundland can reach 41°F (5°C) in winter. In contrast, the waters of the Gulf Stream a few miles away can be a balmy 64°F (18°C). The boundary where the two currents meet is often surrounded in fog, as warm, moist air from the south meets cold air from the north.

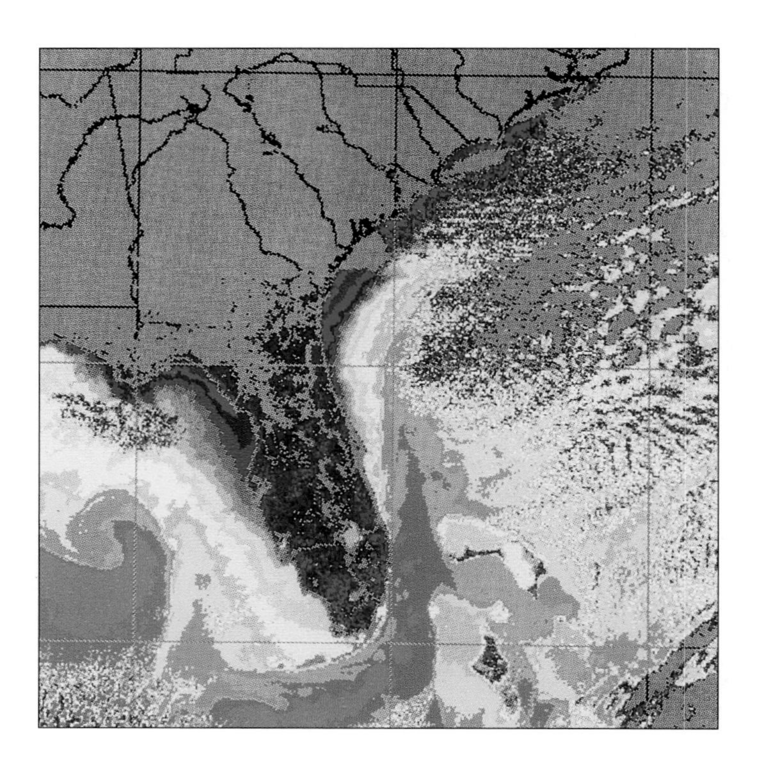

The Gulf Stream is shown by the large area of yellow moving eastward across the Atlantic Ocean.

East of the Grand Banks, the Gulf Stream is called the North Atlantic Current or North Atlantic Drift. There it weakens and branches off in three directions. One branch flows northward past Scotland, warming the climate of northern Europe. Another branch, the Azores Current, flows eastward toward Spain. The rest of the North Atlantic Current turns southward to feed the slow, clockwise circulation of Atlantic waters.

The Gulf Stream was first noted by Spanish sailors in the 16th century. It was later investigated by U.S. scientist and statesman Benjamin Franklin (1706–1790). Space satellites today detect temperature and color variations in the water. They show that the Gulf Stream is a complex network of currents with loops and eddies that shift course over time, rather than a simple ribbon of moving water.

CHECK THESE OUT!

✔ATLANTIC OCEAN ✔OCEAN ✔OCEAN CURRENT

Halogen

The most reactive nonmetals of the periodic table

Fluorine, chlorine, bromine, iodine, and astatine are the elements that form group 17 (VIIA) of the periodic table. These elements are called halogens, from the Greek words *hals* and *genes*, meaning "salt" and "born." They have this name because they form many of the common salts when they combine with metals (table salt—sodium chloride—is an example). The halogens are found in minerals and seawater. Their compounds are used to make household and industrial products, including toothpaste, flame-retardant chemicals, and photographic film.

Purple iodine crystals sublime—turn directly from solid to vapor—on contact with air.

Physical properties

The halogens have the most varied physical properties of all the groups of the periodic table. Their depth of color increases from the lightest to the heaviest member of the group, as do their melting and boiling points. Fluorine is a pale yellow gas that forms a liquid at –306°F (–188.2°C). Chlorine is a yellow-green gas that forms a liquid at –30.6°F (–34.7°C). Bromine is a brownish-purple liquid, and iodine is a dark violet solid. Astatine is too radioactive for a large sample to exist, but is believed to be a metallic gray solid. The stable halogens exist as diatomic molecules, such as F_2 and Cl_2.

HIGHLIGHTS

- In order of increasing size, the halogens are fluorine, chlorine, bromine, iodine, and astatine.
- The halogens are oxidizing agents that are poisonous to living organisms.
- Astatine is an extremely unstable element that can only be made in a particle accelerator.

Discovery

In 1774, Swedish chemist Carl Wilhelm Scheele (1742–1786) prepared chlorine by mixing hydrochloric acid and manganese dioxide. He thought he had made a compound of oxygen. However, in 1810, British chemist Sir Humphry Davy (1778–1829) repeated Scheele's experiment and named the product chlorine, from the Greek word *chloros*, meaning "greenish yellow." French chemist Bernard Courtois (1777–1838) discovered iodine as he was washing seaweed with acid in 1811. The element appeared as dark violet fumes. In 1813, French chemist Joseph Gay-Lussac (1778–1850) confirmed the existence of the element and named it from the Greek word *iodes*, meaning "violet colored."

The next halogen to be identified was bromine. It was discovered in 1826 by French chemist Antoine-Jérôme Balard (1802–1876). He was working with the liquid left after sodium chloride and sodium sulfate had been crystallized

Gases containing halogens were used as weapons during World War I (1914–1918).

STORY OF SCIENCE

Chlorine Poisons

In 1939, Swiss chemist Paul Müller (1899–1965) discovered the pesticidal properties of DDT. This is an organochlorine (a compound that contains carbon, hydrogen, and chlorine). For more than 30 years, huge quantities of DDT were sprayed worldwide to kill pests that damaged crops and spread diseases such as malaria. Then, in 1962, U.S marine biologist Rachel Carson (1907–1964) published a book called *Silent Spring*. In her book, she suggested that DDT was entering the food chain and causing reproductive disorders, such as thin-shelled chickens' eggs that would break open when laid.

DDT collects in the body. It dissolves well in fat but does not dissolve in urine, so it is not expelled in bodily wastes. By 1973, concern about the effects of DDT was such that its general use was banned in the United States.

In the 1970s, another group of organochlorine compounds—the dioxins—started to hit the headlines. Between 1965 and 1970, the U.S. military had used an herbicide called Agent Orange to destroy natural jungle cover in the Vietnam War. Agent Orange was a mixture of herbicides. The mixture also contained TCDD (dioxin). A number of health problems in personnel who had handled Agent Orange led to the discovery of the full toxic effects of dioxin. TCDD is now treated as a superpoison, listed as being around 1,000 times more toxic than potassium cyanide. It causes skin complaints, organ disorders, psychiatric illness, birth defects, and possibly cancer.

from water from salt marshes. When he treated the water with chlorine, the liquid turned brown. He later confirmed that the product was an element. The name bromine comes from the Greek word *bromos*, meaning "stench."

Fluorine was discovered much later, in 1886, by French chemist Henri Mossain (1852–1907). He prepared the element by the electrolysis (the use of an electrical current to decompose a compound into its elements) of liquid hydrogen fluoride with dissolved potassium fluoride. The name comes from fluorspar, a fluorine mineral.

Astatine was first made in 1940. A team led by Italian-born U.S. physicist Emilio Segrè (1905–1989) prepared the first few atoms of astatine 211 by bombarding bismuth atoms with alpha particles in a particle accelerator. Astatine does not occur in nature, since it only exists for a few hours at most. Its name comes from *astatos*, the Greek word meaning "unstable."

Chemical properties

All the halogens react with metals to form salts. They do this by taking electrons from metal atoms. In the process, diatomic halogen molecules break up and form ions with a single negative charge. The metal is oxidized, which means it loses electrons. An element that causes oxidation is termed an oxidizing agent. Fluorine is the most powerfully oxidizing of the halogens. It even forms compounds with the unreactive noble gas xenon. Iodine is the least powerful oxidant of the group. The oxidizing power of the halogens makes them poisonous to living things, since they break up living tissue by oxidation.

Halogens react with hydrogen to make hydrogen halides (HAY-lydz) that form acid solutions in water. An example is hydrogen chloride, which forms hydrochloric acid in water. The hydrohalic acids react with metals such as zinc to form hydrogen plus metal halides.

Halogens form a variety of compounds with hydrocarbons. They do this either by adding to a multiple bond or by displacing another atom, often hydrogen. The products contain carbon-halogen bonds. Fluorine forms the strongest bonds with carbon, followed by chlorine, bromine, and then iodine.

Extraction and uses

Fluorine is produced by the electrolysis of liquid hydrogen fluoride that contains potassium fluoride. Treating fluorspar, CaF_2, with sulfuric acid makes the hydrogen fluoride. It is used to make PTFE (polytetrafluoroethene) for use as a nonstick coating called Teflon and for making low-friction bearings, tapes, tubes, and valves that resist chemical attack. Fluorine is also used to make uranium hexafluoride, UF_6, as part of the process to isolate uranium fuel for nuclear power plants. Compounds of fluorine in toothpaste and drinking water help prevent tooth decay.

The light-reacting part of photographic film is made of crystals of silver bromide.

LOOK CLOSER

CFCs and the Ozone Layer

In 1973, Mexican-born U.S. chemist Mario José Molina (born 1943) and U.S. chemist F. Sherwood Rowland (born 1927) started to study the effects of chlorofluorocarbons (CFCs) on the atmosphere. They found that CFCs rose into the stratosphere, some 9 to 15 miles (14.5 to 24 km) above Earth's surface. They proposed that sunlight would be able to break down CFCs and form free chlorine atoms. Each chlorine atom would then be able to destroy up to 100,000 molecules of ozone, the gas that shields Earth's surface from ultraviolet radiation in sunlight. In the 1980s, satellite images revealed a hole in the ozone layer over Antarctica.

In 1987, the United Nations passed an international protocol (diplomatic agreement) to eliminate the production and nonessential use of CFCs. However, CFCs take from 50 to 100 years to decompose in the atmosphere, so the effects of the ozone hole, such as increased risks of skin cancer, will continue to be felt for a while.

Chlorine is extracted by the electrolysis of table salt, NaCl. It is used to sterilize water and to bleach paper and textiles. Organic compounds of chlorine include many solvents and plastics, as well as antiseptics, herbicides, and pesticides. For many years, chlorine and fluorine were used to make chlorofluorocarbon (CFC) refrigerants and aerosol propellants.

Bromine is made by oxidizing seawater with chlorine. Organic compounds of bromine are used in flame-resistant surface coatings and treatments for fabrics. Silver bromide is photosensitive—it decomposes (breaks up) to form bromine and crystals of silver when exposed to light, so it is used to make photographic film, plates, and paper.

Iodine is produced from impurities in sodium nitrate deposits and seaweed. It is used to sterilize wounds and treat thyroid conditions.

CHECK THESE OUT!

✔CHEMICAL REACTION ✔ELEMENT ✔PERIODIC TABLE

Heat

The form of energy that flows from warmer objects to cooler ones

The type of energy that makes things hot or cold is called heat. The idea of heat explains how energy is made and used in human bodies, in the engines of machines such as automobiles, and in power plants. Heat was once thought to be a mysterious fluid that flowed from place to place. Today's scientists believe that when an object is heated, its atoms (the building blocks of chemical elements) and molecules (MAH-luh-KYOOLS; atoms bonded together) move about more quickly. This theory helps to explain many different aspects of the way heat behaves.

HIGHLIGHTS

- Heat is a type of energy that is stored inside a substance; temperature is a measure of how hot or cold something is.
- When heat enters an object, its atoms and molecules move more energetically. Because energy of movement is called kinetic energy, the modern theory of heat is sometimes called the kinetic theory.
- The coldest theoretically possible temperature, at which all heat has been removed from an object, is called absolute zero (–459.67°F, –273.15°C, 0K).
- Heat is transferred by processes called conduction, convection, and radiation.

Heat and temperature

Heat and temperature are often confused, but there is an important difference between them. Heat is a measure of how much energy an object has inside it. Temperature is a measure of how hot or cold something is. What is the difference? If a blow torch is used to supply exactly the same amount of heat energy to a copper pipe and to a jug of water, the pipe will reach a much higher temperature than the water. Both substances will have gained the same amount of heat, but they will have reached different temperatures.

Like any other type of energy, heat can be transferred from one object to another and from place to place. However, the way heat

The way that heat is distributed in the human body can be shown using a thermogram. The hottest parts are red; the coldest are black.

EVERYDAY SCIENCE

Keeping Warm: Convection and Insulation

The ability of a substance to conduct heat is called its thermal conductivity. To keep an object cooler or hotter than its environment, people try to enclose it in a material of low thermal conductivity, sometimes called insulation. A vacuum (VA-KYOOM; empty space) has the lowest, but not zero, conductivity because heat can travel through a vacuum by radiation. Vacuum flasks keep drinks hot or cold by using a pair of glass bottles separated by a vacuum. Air has low thermal conductivity but must be trapped in cloth or a polymer foam to eliminate convection if it is to be used as insulation. Wearing several thin layers of clothing is much warmer than wearing one thick layer because of the insulation (air) between the layers.

Another way of keeping warm is by generating heat and circulating it around a room. A space heater warms the air above it, which rises and moves toward the ceiling. Cool air is sucked in from below and heated in its turn. Eventually, this sets up a loop of rising and falling air called a convection current that rapidly warms the room.

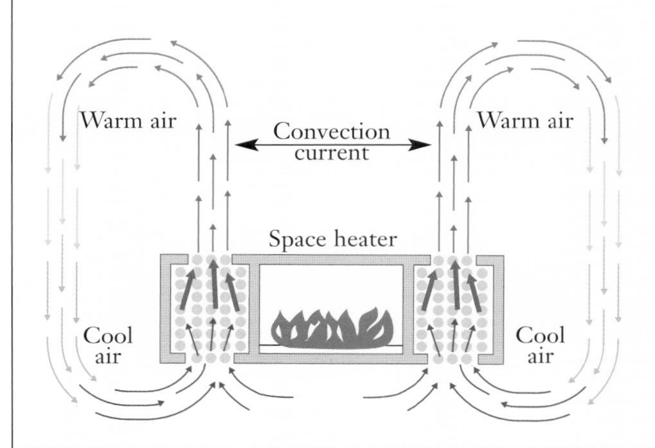

A space heater (left) sets up a convection current of warm, rising air in order to heat a room. Cooler air enters the heater from below and is, in turn, heated. In a thermos flask (right), a vacuum between the inner and outer bottles helps prevent the transfer of heat.

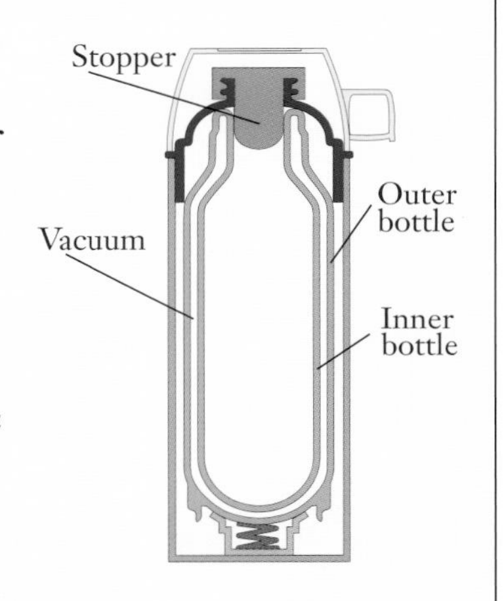

is transferred and the direction in which it flows depends on the temperature. Heat always flows from a hotter object to a colder one, never the other way. Inside a hot object, atoms and molecules are constantly moving around. Adding more heat makes the atoms and molecules move more energetically. Heat is a kind of kinetic (kuh-NEH-tik) energy (energy of movement).

Measuring heat and temperature

Heat and temperature are measured in different ways, using different units. Heat is measured in units called calories (KAH-luh-reez). One calorie is defined as the amount of heat needed to raise the temperature of 1 g of water by 1.8°F (1°C). Scientists tend to use an alternative metric unit called the joule (J) to measure heat and all other types of energy. One calorie equals 4.184 joules. These calories are different from the Calories used to measure amounts of food energy, which are written with a capital C and are really kilocalories (thousands of calories).

Temperature is measured using different temperature scales, notably Fahrenheit (FAR-uhn-HYT) and Celsius (SEL-see-uhs; often also called centigrade). These scales are based around two different, conveniently measured temperatures called the fixed points. In the Fahrenheit scale, the fixed points are the freezing point of water (32°F) and the boiling point of water (212°F). In the Celsius (centigrade) scale, the same points are represented by the temperatures 0°C (freezing) and 100°C (boiling).

The Kelvin (absolute) temperature scale is widely used by scientists and is worked out in a different way. It is based on the idea that there is an absolute zero of temperature at which the atoms and molecules in a substance have the minimum possible kinetic energy because they no longer have any heat energy. This temperature,

0K (no degree sign is used with the Kelvin scale), is equivalent to –459.67°F or –273.15°C. No one has ever cooled anything to absolute zero, but scientists have reached temperatures to within a very tiny fraction of a degree of it.

Heat capacity

The same amount of heat will raise the temperature of different substances by different amounts. For example, 10 calories of heat will raise the temperature of 0.035 oz (1 g) of water by 18°F (10°C). However, 10 calories of heat will heat up the same amount of copper by 218°F (111°C). The amount of heat needed to raise the temperature of a certain amount of a particular substance by a certain temperature is called its specific heat capacity (or simply, specific heat).

Water has a specific heat capacity that is 11 times greater than that of copper. Copper therefore heats up much more easily than water. However, a certain amount of water can store much more heat energy than the same amount of copper. This is why water is used to store heat in domestic heating and hot water systems, while copper is used to line the bottoms of cooking pans so they heat up more quickly. A hot water system made from a solid block of copper would store far less energy than a tank of hot water, and it would cool down very quickly. Equally, a cooking pan made of ice (if that were possible) would take too long to transfer heat.

DISCOVERERS

James Prescott Joule

British physicist James Prescott Joule (1818–1889) finally confirmed that heat was not an unusual substance but just another form of energy. In a famous series of experiments, he showed that apparently different types of energy were really the same thing. In each case he proved that a certain amount of electrical or mechanical energy could be converted (changed) into exactly the same amount of heat, also proving that heat was a type of energy, too. Joule's important contribution to the understanding of heat was eventually recognized when scientists decided to name the joule, the scientific unit of energy, in his honor.

Heat transfer

Heat moves from hot objects to colder ones by processes called conduction, convection, and radiation. Conduction means that heat is transferred when a hot object touches a colder one. If a copper rod is thrust into a fire, copper atoms at the hot end of the rod begin to vibrate more energetically. This makes them strike neighboring atoms, passing some of their energy on, and causing those atoms to vibrate more energetically as well. Gradually, heat energy is transferred all along the copper rod.

Convection is a different form of heat transfer that involves a liquid or gas carrying heat away from a hot solid. The air above a hot stove warms, rises, and circulates around the room. As it does so, colder air replaces it and is itself warmed and circulated. An invisible conveyor belt of heat called a convection current is slowly set up and warms all the air in the room. The liquid in a hot pan on the top of a stove warms, rises, and circulates in the same way. Convection is also the process by which heat pushes hot molten rock around inside Earth, helping to form many of the planet's geological features.

The other main type of heat transfer is called radiation. Hot objects give off a type of electromagnetic wave called infrared radiation. This is similar to light, only it has a longer wavelength (lower frequency). Although infrared is invisible to human eyes, it can be detected by electronic instruments such as night vision binoculars. These instruments can detect moving objects in complete darkness by picking up the heat they give off.

Latent heat

Heating an object usually causes its temperature to rise, but this is not always the case. If ice is heated to its melting point of 32°F (0°C) and extra heat is then supplied to turn it into water,

LOOK CLOSER

Radiation: Heating by the Sun

The way the Sun heats Earth is an example of heat transfer by radiation. The average rate at which Earth receives energy in this way is called the solar constant. This constant—about 13 calories per square inch (2 calories per sq cm) per minute—is calculated by measuring the energy received by a small area on Earth's surface for a certain period of time. Estimates suggest that the total solar energy reaching Earth every second is roughly the same as the energy that could be produced from three million tons of oil.

the temperature of the ice–water mixture remains the same even though more heat is being supplied. This curious result applies when a substance changes from a solid to a liquid or from a liquid to a gas. It is called a phase change because solids, liquids, and gases are also called the phases of matter. The explanation is quite simple. It takes energy to turn ice into water because the solid crystalline structure of ice must be broken apart to make liquid water. So, although heat is constantly being supplied, it is used to push apart the water molecules rather than to raise the temperature. A certain amount of heat is needed to turn a certain amount of solid into a liquid. This is called the latent (LAY-tuhnt) heat of fusion. The same amount of heat is released when the liquid turns back into a solid.

History of the study of heat

Heat was once thought to be an invisible fluid called *caloric* (kah-LAWR-ik). French chemist Antoine Lavoisier (1743–1794) thought that an object heated up when caloric flowed into it and cooled down when caloric flowed out. If a hot object touched a cooler one, caloric flowed out of the hot object into the cooler one. This theory fell out of favor toward the end of the 1700s when experiments by British physicist Benjamin Thompson (Count Rumford; 1753–1814) and British chemist Sir Humphry Davy (1778–1829) suggested that heat could be converted (changed) into other forms of energy. This new theory was finally confirmed in the 1840s by British physicist James Prescott Joule (1818–1889).

Many other scientists played a vital role in the modern understanding of heat. Scottish chemist Joseph Black (1728–1799) helped to explain the difference between temperature and heat. Black worked out that different substances have different specific heat capacities. He also set out the theory of latent heat. Today's kinetic theory of heat, which explains heat as the movement of atoms and molecules, developed from the work of many scientists, including Austrian physicist Ludwig Boltzman (1844–1906) and British physicist James Clerk Maxwell (1831–1879).

Temperature scales date to around 1714. The Fahrenheit scale was proposed by German physicist Daniel Fahrenheit (1686–1736), who developed thermometers (thuhr-MAH-muh-tuhrs) made of alcohol and mercury. The Celsius scale was named for Swedish astronomer Anders Celsius (1701–1744) in 1742. The Kelvin scale, named for British physicist Lord Kelvin (William Thompson; 1824–1907), was adopted by scientists in 1933.

CHECK THESE OUT!

✔CRYOGENICS ✔ELECTROMAGNETIC SPECTRUM
✔ENERGY ✔INFRARED RADIATION ✔TEMPERATURE

Helium

A light, unreactive gas that is the second most common element in the Universe

The lightest and most common element in the Universe is hydrogen. The second lightest and the second most common element is helium. It was discovered by looking out into space but is rare on Earth. Today, helium can be isolated from natural gas, and it has a variety of uses.

Helium atoms have a very simple structure. At the center is a nucleus containing two positively charged protons and two uncharged neutrons. The nucleus is orbited by a pair of negatively charged electrons. Most elements take part in chemical reactions to gain or lose electrons and reach a stable pattern. The pair of electrons in helium is already very stable, so helium does not take part in reactions and is called a noble gas.

Helium is a very light gas, much lighter than air. Helium released into Earth's atmosphere floats to the top and very gradually escapes into space. Helium's lightness also means that it has the lowest boiling point of any substance, at –452°F (–269°C), which is just 7°F (4°C) above absolute zero, the coldest temperature possible.

Discovery of helium

Helium was discovered in 1868 by British astronomer Norman Lockyer (1836–1920), who devoted his time to spectrography, the study of light by splitting it into a spectrum (range of different colors). During a solar eclipse, Lockyear studied the light from atoms in the chromosphere, the Sun's thin atmosphere. This light comes from just a few different elements producing light of very precise colors. Lockyer used these colors to identify the elements in the Sun's atmosphere. However, he found that the chromosphere was also producing yellow light with a color he could not link to any known element. He named this new element helium after the Greek for the Sun, *helios*.

Today's astronomers know that stars, such as the Sun, produce helium as they shine by combining together hydrogen atoms. Something similar happened in the big bang that created the Universe. As a result, 10 percent of material in the Universe is helium.

Manufacture and uses

Helium is extracted from natural gas reserves where it has been trapped for millions of years underground. Helium is often used for its lightness or low boiling point. Because it is so much lighter than air, helium is used to fill airships and balloons. It is much safer than the highly explosive hydrogen. Liquid helium, the coldest substance known, is also used for cooling electronic circuits and other scientific equipment.

Divers use helium in their air tanks to replace the nitrogen that makes up ordinary air. Nitrogen can cause severe problems when breathed in at the high pressures in deep-sea diving. The squeaky voice that a diver gets while breathing helium is the only minor side effect.

CHECK THESE OUT!
✔DENSITY ✔GAS

Balloons that are filled with helium float well because helium is so much lighter than air.

Holography

A type of three-dimensional photography

The science of making holograms (three-dimensional photographs) is called holography. Unlike a flat, two-dimensional photograph, a hologram seems to have depth and appears to rotate when you move your head to look around it. Although they were first thought of in 1948, the technology for making holograms did not emerge until the 1960s. They have many uses, including tiny security devices used to protect credit cards against forgery.

Photographs, eyes, and holograms

Photographic film is a piece of flat plastic coated with a chemical that is sensitive to light. When a photograph is taken, light from objects in front of the camera is focused on the film. The chemical coating of the film is changed into a pattern that corresponds to the scene in front of the camera. As the camera has only one lens, it can record only patterns of light and dark.

> **HIGHLIGHTS**
>
> - Holograms are three-dimensional images stored on photographic film and played back with a laser.
> - A hologram of an object is produced by splitting a laser beam in two. Half of the beam is bounced off the object onto a photographic film; the other half of the beam is shone directly onto the film.
> - Holograms have many uses, including making jewelry and protecting credit cards.

Looking at a hologram is just like looking at the original three-dimensional object.

A hologram stores not just the pattern of light and dark, like a photograph, but also information about the distance the light rays have traveled from points on the object. A hologram is not simply a frozen image of a scene at one moment, like a photograph, but a type of active record of exactly how light waves were being reflected away from the object at that moment. Looking at a photograph is like looking at a drawing, but looking at a hologram is like being transported back to the moment when it was produced.

Making holograms

A hologram is made by bouncing the light from a laser off an object onto a photographic plate (a piece of glass similar to the film in a camera). The laser beam is first split into two separate beams. One of these beams, the reference beam, is bounced off a mirror onto the photographic

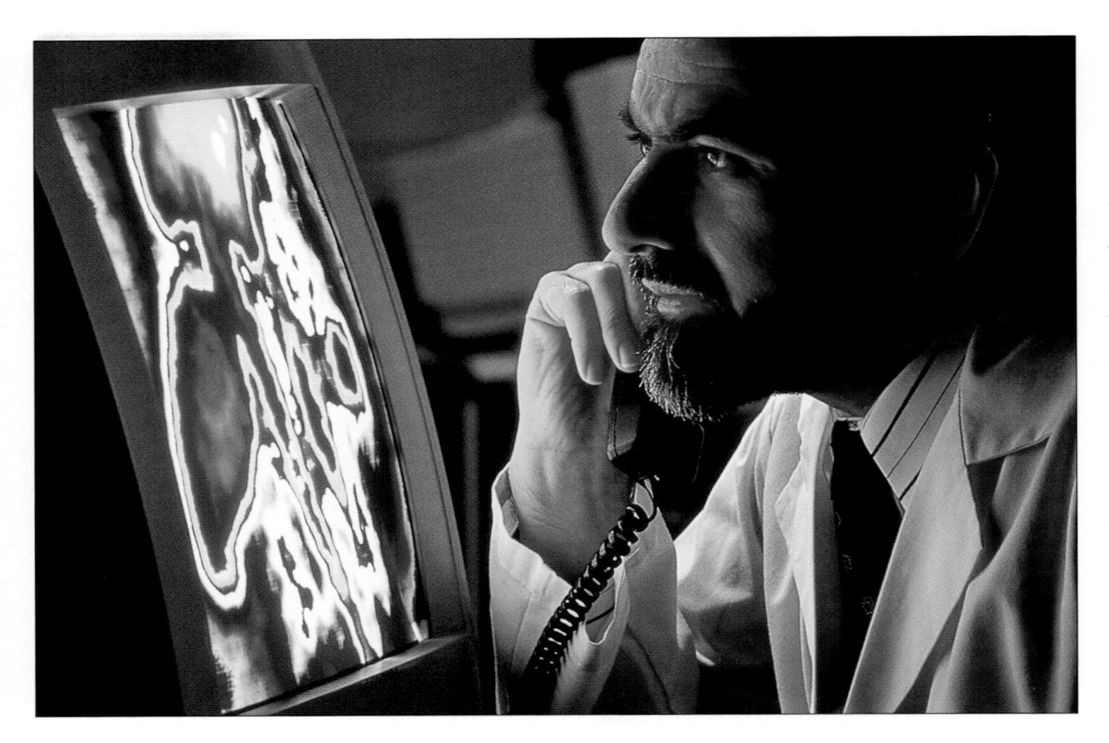

Doctors can use holograms to examine patients without having to cut them open.

plate. The other beam, called the object beam, is directed at the object, which reflects part of the beam onto the plate.

If no object were present, the object and reference beams would be identical when they arrived at the plate. The shape of the object changes the way the object beam is reflected, so it arrives slightly out of synchronization (SIN-kruh-nuh-ZAY-shuhn; exact timing) with the reference beam. When the object and reference beams combine on the photographic plate, they interfere with one another. For example, crests (maximums) in the light waves from the object beam may combine with troughs (minimums) in the light waves from the reference beam, canceling each other out. Alternatively, crests and troughs in both beams may join with one another to produce bigger crests and troughs on the plate. This process of interference produces a record in the photographic plate of exactly how the object reflects light waves. This is the secret to being able to reproduce a three-dimensional image later on.

In constructive interference (below), light waves join up to make bigger waves. In destructive interference (below right), waves cancel each other out.

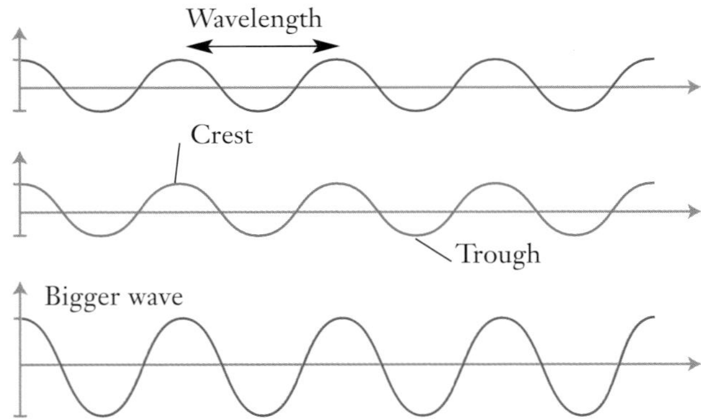

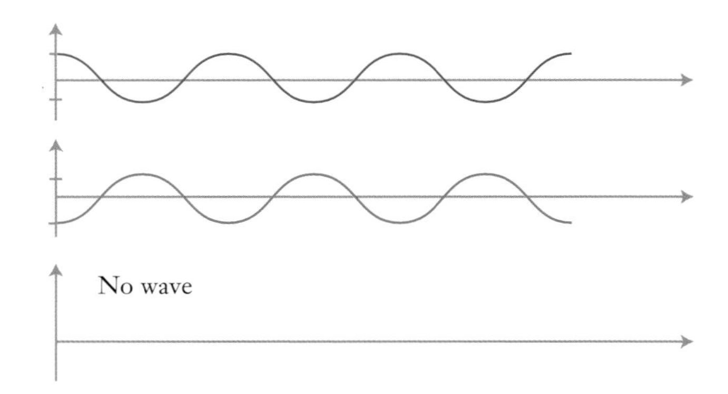

Lasers

Why is a laser used to produce a hologram rather than an ordinary light such as a flashlight? A hologram is designed to be a record of how an object reflects light waves in different ways. To work out what effect the object has had on the light, all the light waves need to be traveling the same way at the beginning. In a flashlight, the light waves are incoherent—different light waves set off at different times, so the peaks of some waves leave with the troughs of others. Using a flashlight as the reference beam in holography would not work. It would be impossible to tell what effect the object had had on these jumbled-up, incoherent light waves. A laser, however, produces light in a very precise and regular way. All the light waves are coherent—the peaks of all the waves leave at the same time. Therefore, it is easier to tell what effect the object has had on the reflected laser beam.

Viewing holograms

A hologram made in this way is not very interesting to look at because it is just a piece of glass covered with light and dark areas. That piece of glass contains a secret, however, and with the help of another laser beam, its secret can be revealed. Shining a laser onto a hologram changes the laser beam so that it is exactly the same as the original laser beam reflected from the object used to make the hologram in the first place. In other words, there is no difference between the hologram and the original object. Looking from side to side at the hologram is just like looking at the original object. The hologram recreates the original object.

Lasers can be inconvenient, expensive, and hazardous to the eye. Fortunately, not all holograms have to be viewed in this way. Some types of holograms can be reproduced in ordinary daylight. This discovery has led to some important and interesting uses of holograms in industry and also in entertainment.

Uses of holograms

Putting holograms onto credit cards has successfully deterred counterfeiters because making holograms is difficult and expensive. Holograms are also widely used for entertainment and decoration, such as making holographic keyrings and jewelry. A hologram of British actor Laurence Olivier was even used in a 1987 theater production, partly for the effect and partly so the 80-year-old actor did not need to appear on stage every night. Some scientists believe holography could be a good way of making televisions and movies three-dimensional.

Holography is a very precise technique. This precision has found some important industrial uses. One method compares the difference between an object and its hologram after some change has taken place. For example, a hologram could be made of one of the turbine blades in an airplane engine. After the engine has been flying for some time, the technique may be used to compare the blade with its hologram. This reveals any changes that may have taken place since the original hologram was made.

LOOK CLOSER

Splitting Beams

Lasers are usually needed both to create and to reproduce holograms. To create a hologram, a laser beam is split into two beams, an object beam that reflects off the object and a reference beam that bounces off a mirror. When the two beams combine on a photographic plate, the result is a hologram.

Reproducing a hologram involves shining a laser onto or through it. This procedure changes the laser beam so it looks like the original beam reflected from the object when the hologram was made. There is no difference between the beam from the hologram and the beam from the original object. Therefore, a hologram looks just like the original object, whichever way it is viewed.

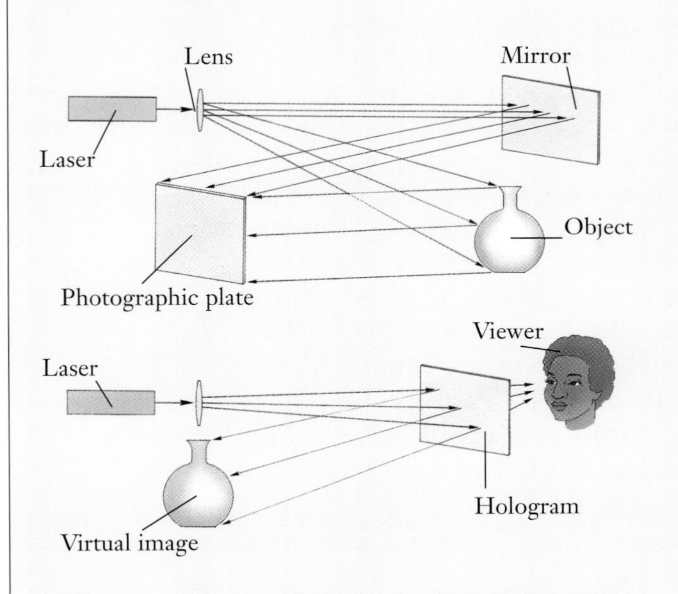

The apparatus used to make a hologram (top) is different from the apparatus used to produce images from one (bottom).

CHECK THESE OUT!
✔LASER ✔LIGHT ✔OPTICS ✔WAVES

Hubble Space Telescope

A multipurpose astronomical observatory that orbits Earth

Astronomers get their clearest view of the depths of the Universe by using the Hubble Space Telescope (HST). The telescope was launched in 1990. It has made hundreds of astronomical discoveries and has been visited three times by astronauts on repair missions.

The Edwin P. Hubble Space Telescope (its full name) is a huge instrument that orbits (circles around) Earth at an altitude of 380 miles (610 km). The telescope is 43 feet (13.1 m) long. It has wings of solar panels on either side to create the power it needs to operate.

Like all modern astronomical telescopes, the HST is a reflector. Light entering the telescope tube is collected by a curved primary mirror at the other end. This reflects the light back to a smaller, secondary mirror halfway up the telescope. The primary mirror is 94½ inches (2.4 m) long. The smaller convex mirror is 12½ inches (31 cm) long. From the secondary mirror, the light bounces back through a hole in the center of the primary to the electronic instruments at the back of the telescope.

HIGHLIGHTS

- The HST can focus light at several different instruments to produce an image or to split light into a spectrum.
- The HST's view is much clearer than Earth-based telescopes because it is above the atmosphere.
- When the HST was launched in 1990, it had a flaw in the mirror that had to be corrected later.

The HST holds different instruments. The light collected by the telescope can be sent to any one of these instruments through a system of mirrors behind the primary mirror. These instruments include cameras, spectrometers (instruments that split the light by wavelength from distant objects in order to identify the elements that produced it), and detectors for recording ultraviolet light. Although the HST is designed mainly for collecting visible light, it can also be used as an ultraviolet telescope.

The Hubble Space Telescope is controlled from the Space Telescope Science Institute at Baltimore, Maryland. Astronomers from around the world go to the institute to spend time using one of the world's most powerful telescopes. Their instructions are routed through NASA's Goddard Space Flight Center to the HST itself.

Often the telescope will take one single long-exposure image of a distant star or galaxy, lasting several hours, in order to capture more detail. It is important, therefore, that the telescope is controlled very accurately. This is carried out by a series of gyroscopes (JY-roh-SKOHPS; freely spinning wheels) that monitor and correct any changes in the telescope's position, and sensors that lock on to bright stars and make sure they are not moving relative to the telescope.

HST's history

The idea of putting a telescope into space dates back to 1946, when it was suggested by U.S. astronomer Lyman Spitzer (born 1914). Spitzer realized that a telescope beyond the atmosphere would get a much clearer view of the Universe. NASA did not begin building the HST until 1977. The telescope was designed by a team of scientists from NASA and the European Space Agency ESA. It was ready for launch in 1986, when the explosion of the Space Shuttle *Challenger* brought the U.S. space program to a halt. The telescope was finally launched from the shuttle *Discovery* in April 1990. It was one of the shuttle's largest ever cargoes, weighing 25,000 pounds (11,340 kg).

As soon as the HST went into operation, however, its designers realized there was a serious problem. The primary mirror was not focusing light correctly, and all the images from the telescope appeared blurred. The mirror had been ground to slightly the wrong shape. The amount of error was tiny, just 0.002 mm, but it was enough to paralyze the telescope. Computer software was able to correct some of the problems, but the telescope needed a repair mission before it could operate properly.

In December 1993, the shuttle *Endeavour* met up with the HST in space, and the crew carried out a complex repair operation. One of the instrument pods was removed and replaced with a unit called COSTAR. By passing light from the telescope through a complex system of mirrors, COSTAR corrected the fault and allowed the rest of the HST's instruments to function perfectly.

Since then, the telescope has had two more servicing missions. These are necessary to repair and update its astronomical instruments. They are also used to replace the solar panels, sensors, and gyroscopes that keep the telescope working. Just before the 1999 servicing mission, the telescope was put out of action for several weeks when its gyroscopic guidance system failed.

With continuing regular service missions, the Hubble Space Telescope is expected to work up to and beyond the end of its expected life span in 2005. In the longer term, NASA is already planning the HST's successor, the Next Generation Space Telescope (NGST), with a vast 26-foot (8-m) mirror, for an expected launch in 2008.

The HST has viewed objects more distant than any ground-based telescopes have been able to observe.

LOOK CLOSER

Major Finds

Everywhere it has looked, the HST has made astounding discoveries and returned spectacular pictures to Earth. In 1996 it produced the first map of Pluto, the most distant planet in the Solar System, which is 3.7 billion miles (5.9 billion km) from the Sun. Beyond the Solar System, astronomers have used it to see stars forming and dying. The HST has also studied galaxies colliding and discovered black holes in the centers of some galaxies.

In 1999, the telescope finally achieved one of its main aims—to measure the rate of the Universe's expansion. The HST's measurements finally settled the arguments over the rate of expansion, called the Hubble Constant. Using this constant to trace the movement of the Universe back through time, astronomers can also find the age of the Universe—estimated at around 12 billion years.

CHECK THESE OUT!

✔NASA ✔SATELLITE ✔SPACE
✔SPACE SCIENCE ✔ULTRAVIOLET RADIATION

Humidity

The measure of the amount of water vapor in the atmosphere

Why does an air temperature of 70°F (21°C) in Florida feel so much hotter than an air temperature of 70°F (21°C) in Arizona? The answer is humidity, which is the measure of the amount of water vapor in the atmosphere. Humans keep cool by the evaporation (the change from liquid to vapor) of their sweat. If the humidity is high, sweat evaporates more slowly, and so humans feel hotter. Florida is almost surrounded by water, and it also has a large volume of water inland. Heat causes the water to evaporate. Arizona, by contrast, is a very dry region surrounded by land.

The amount of water vapor that the air can hold varies with temperature and atmospheric pressure. When the atmosphere holds as much moisture as possible at a certain temperature, it is said to be saturated (SA-chuh-RAY-tuhd). At any particular temperature, the amount of water vapor in the air, compared to the amount required for saturation, is called the relative humidity. So, for example, if the air contains only half the vapor that it could hold when saturated, the relative humidity is 50 percent.

In a location where the relative humidity in the afternoon is 50 percent, when the temperature drops at night, the relative humidity may rise to as much as 90 percent—although the

HIGHLIGHTS

- The amount of water vapor in the air varies with temperature and atmospheric pressure.
- When the atmosphere holds the maximum water vapor at a particular temperature, it is said to be saturated and relative humidity is 100 percent.
- The amount of water vapor actually in the air, compared with that in saturated air, is called the relative humidity.
- The dew point is the cooling temperature at which the air is saturated, and water vapor begins to condense back into liquid.
- Relative humidity can be controlled indoors by air conditioning.
- Conditions of high humidity are uncomfortable because human perspiration evaporates slowly.

A jungle mist in Eastern Cameroon, an area that is near the equator and has a high relative humidity. Mists frequently form overnight.

amount of water vapor in the air has not changed. The relative humidity has changed because cold air can hold less water. Normally the air is never completely saturated. If it is, then mist, fog, rain, or snow can result.

Rain or snow usually falls when air masses rise rapidly and are cooled below the temperature of saturation. The temperature at which water vapor begins to condense back into liquid is called the dew point. The dew point is always lower than the air temperature, unless the air is already saturated. The closer the dew point is to the air temperature, the more likely it is that mist or fog will form. This happens when the air at ground level is saturated, and the temperature then drops.

Relative humidity is high near the equator, and between 40 and 60 degrees of latitude (the distance from the equator), where the dew point and air temperature are usually close together. Relative humidity is low in the desert zones of subtropical high pressure, where the difference between dew point and air temperature is large.

Vapor pressure

Vapor pressure is a measure of the tendency of liquid water to change into its gaseous state of water vapor. The water vapor in the atmosphere exerts (puts into action) a pressure, and the moisture content of the air is measured in terms of this pressure. The total air pressure is the sum of two partial pressures: that of the water vapor and that of the dry air with which it is mixed.

For any given temperature, there is a maximum vapor pressure. Above this temperature, the vapor condenses into water droplets or forms small ice crystals. This is the saturation vapor pressure. The relative humidity is defined as the actual vapor pressure divided by the saturation vapor pressure.

Instruments used to measure humidity are called hygrometers (hy-GRAH-muh-tuhrz). Mechanical hygrometers rely upon the principle that organic (carbon- and hydrogen-containing) substances, such as human hair, will contract or stretch according to the relative humidity. The meters are attached to a spring that is connected to an indicator needle. Movement of the substance makes the needle move against a humidity scale, giving a reading.

Other types of hygrometers use substances that react in a different way to changes in relative humidity. They are used to detect humidity-related changes in electrical resistance, transparency, weight, or volume.

A barometer (buh-RAH-muh-tuhr; instrument for measuring atmospheric pressure) reacts to changes in the total atmospheric pressure. It does not directly measure humidity, but it shows when the air pressure is changing, due to changing amounts of water vapor.

LOOK CLOSER

Air Conditioning

Air conditioning controls air temperature and relative humidity indoors. However, the most desirable conditions can vary greatly from country to country. In the United States and Canada, an indoor temperature of 65°F (18°C) and a relative humidity of 40 to 60 percent is usual. In Great Britain a temperature of 72°F (22°C) and a relative humidity of 50 to 60 percent is preferred.

Many industrial plants, such as printing works, also need air conditioning. The size and properties of paper, like hair, change with the humidity. A relative humidity between 40 and 50 percent is best. Keeping the humidity constant ensures that the paper is always the same size for the machinery.

CHECK THESE OUT!

✔ATMOSPHERE ✔EVAPORATION ✔WATER

Hurricane

A fierce and destructive storm caused by rotating winds

Residents of southeastern U.S. states are familiar with the destruction caused by hurricanes. Other parts of the world also suffer similarly violent storms. The storms that develop over the Atlantic Ocean are called hurricanes. Those that begin in the western Pacific Ocean are called typhoons. Storms that begin in the Indian Ocean are called tropical cyclones. These storms all develop over the oceans in areas where the atmospheric pressure is low.

HIGHLIGHTS

- The rotation of Earth causes winds to be deflected from their original direction. This is called the Coriolis effect.
- Areas of low atmospheric pressure form over warm oceans. Water vapor is drawn up from the oceans, lowering the pressure even more and giving up its heat to power the hurricane.
- Damage caused by hurricanes is due to both powerful winds and a storm surge that floods low-lying coastal areas.

How hurricanes develop

Close to the equator (an imaginary line around Earth at equal distances from the North and South Poles), the rotation of Earth causes winds to be deflected (pushed) away from their original direction. In the Northern Hemisphere, the winds are deflected to the right. In the Southern Hemisphere, they are deflected to the left. This process is called the Coriolis effect. Hurricanes are much more common in the Northern Hemisphere.

Other conditions are necessary, however, before the winds develop into a hurricane. If the ocean surface is warm (above 82°F or 28°C), then the atmospheric pressure above it decreases. Air from areas of higher pressure moves in, and the Coriolis effect causes strong circling winds. In the Northern Hemisphere, these winds rotate in a counterclockwise direction around a center, rather like a tornado. In the Southern Hemisphere, the winds rotate in a clockwise direction.

The strong winds draw water vapor from the warm ocean surface and lower the atmospheric pressure. The warm vapor is the source of the hurricane's power. It condenses (is made more compact) in the colder atmosphere and gives up its heat energy to make the winds swirl faster. Thick clouds form and there is heavy rainfall. Once a hurricane reaches land, or colder ocean surfaces, it can no longer draw energy from the water vapor. It loses power rapidly. A steady supply of heat and moisture is necessary to keep the hurricane moving.

On a weather map, a hurricane appears as a set of nearly circular lines, one inside the other. These lines, which are called isobars (EYE-soh-BAHRZ), represent the atmospheric pressure. They are similar to the contour lines on a land map. At the

Hurricanes develop in the Caribbean and western Atlantic area. This photograph shows Hurricane Greta skirting the north shore of Honduras in Central America in 1978.

center (the "eye") of the storm, the pressure is lowest and the temperature is highest. The whole storm system generally has a diameter of about 300 miles (485 km).

When and where hurricanes develop

Hurricane formation is most likely at latitudes above 5 degrees over the tropical oceans and below 30 degrees of latitude. The Coriolis effect is strongest above 5 degrees, but the ocean is not sufficiently warm above 30 degrees.

In the Atlantic Ocean, most hurricanes develop in late summer or early fall, when the ocean water is warmest. The usual areas are the Cape Verde islands, the north and southwest Caribbean, and the Gulf of Mexico. In the Pacific Ocean, the main danger areas include the west coast of Mexico, the China Sea, the south Pacific east of Australia, and the Bay of Bengal.

Hurricane damage

The damage caused by hurricanes is due mainly to two factors: the strength of the very high winds and flooding. The low pressure in the center of the storm and its high temperature cause the ocean water to build up into a huge wave. This wave is called a storm surge and travels with the hurricane. When it reaches land, the storm surge can flood the low-lying areas along the coast. A storm surge caused by a typhoon in the Bay of Bengal, for example, caused 250,000 deaths in Bangladesh in south-central Asia in April 1991.

The danger to human life in the United States is steadily decreasing. What is called the Hurricane of Independence is believed to have killed 4,170 people in 1775. In contrast, 71 people lost their lives in Hurricane Andrew in 1992. Early warning systems now exist, which enable people to evacuate those areas at risk.

Early warning systems rely upon modern satellite technology. The National Weather Service (NWS) uses stationary and orbiting satellites to monitor the weather conditions over the oceans. The agency can detect conditions likely to cause hurricanes and track the development of the storms. Then it can predict when and where the hurricanes will reach land with considerable accuracy.

This damage was caused by Hurricane Andrew. The hurricane devastated the southeast coast of the United States in 1992.

As well as detecting hurricanes, scientists are also able to issue warnings to the public about when and where the hurricanes will strike. The National Oceanic and Atmospheric Administration has also tried seeding clouds with chemicals to make rain, so that a hurricane's power can be reduced before it reaches land.

How and why hurricanes are named

Hurricanes are the only natural disasters to be given human names. Weather scientists suggested that a hurricane developed rather like a person, from its birth over the tropical oceans, to its life as it traveled westward, ending with its death over land or colder ocean waters. The practice of naming began in the 1940s. At that time, the NWS used only female names. Male names began to be used for hurricanes in the 1980s.

Hurricanes are named in alphabetical order, with a different name for the letter chosen each year. The list of names for the year is issued around April, although the hurricane season does not begin before June 1. The same list of names is used every six years. Very large storms keep their names by going down in history. When this happens, a new name is chosen for that letter in later years.

CHECK THESE OUT!

✔METEOROLOGY ✔WEATHER ✔WIND

Hydrocarbon

A compound with molecules containing only hydrogen and carbon atoms

HIGHLIGHTS 

- Alkanes contain only single bonds between carbon atoms. Alkenes have at least one double carbon–carbon bond. Alkynes have a triple bond.
- Aromatic hydrocarbons contain one or more rings of six carbon atoms.
- The carbon atoms in hydrocarbons link together in straight chains, branched chains, and rings.
- Hydrocarbons are useful fuels, solvents, and starting materials for making other chemicals.

An enormous group of chemicals that contain only the elements hydrogen and carbon are called hydrocarbons. They include methane (CH_4), which is natural gas, carotene ($C_{40}H_{50}$), which is an orange pigment in carrots, and polyethylene (PAHL-ee-EHTH-uh-LEEN). Polyethylene is a plastic (used to make plastic bags) with molecules containing thousands of carbon atoms and twice as many hydrogens.

Single and multiple bonds

Each carbon atom forms four chemical bonds to other atoms around it. Of these four bonds, there might be one, two, or three bonds between neighboring carbon atoms. In hydrocarbons, the remaining bonds are taken up by hydrogen atoms, which form one bond each. After methane, which has one carbon atom, the simplest hydrocarbons contain two carbons. In ethane (C_2H_6), the carbon atoms are linked by a single bond. The remaining three bonds on each carbon atom are with hydrogen atoms, so the atoms are grouped as $H_3C\text{-}CH_3$. The double bond between the two carbon atoms in ethene (C_2H_4) leaves only two bonds on each carbon for bonding to hydrogens, and the formula can be written $H_2C{=}CH_2$. Ethyne (acetylene, C_2H_2) has a triple bond between the carbon atoms, which are each bonded to one hydrogen atom. Its formula can be written $HC{\equiv}CH$.

Chains, rings, branches

Carbon is the only element whose atoms can link together in chains and rings. In a straight chain, each carbon atom is linked to two others (apart from carbons at the end). A straight-chain molecule in which the carbon–carbon bonds are all single is called a straight-chain alkane. Alkenes contain at least one double bond and alkynes have at least one triple bond.

A very important class of cyclic hydrocarbons are those called the aromatics by chemists, originally because of their scents, but now because of a type of chemical bonding that they share. Benzene (C_6H_6) is the smallest member of this group, and it has six carbon atoms arranged in a ring, with one hydrogen atom bonded to each carbon atom.

Isomers

Because of the many ways in which hydrogen and carbon atoms can be joined, several different hydrocarbons can share the same formula. These molecules that have the same numbers of atoms of each element in different arrangements are called isomers. The ring compound cyclohexane (C_6H_{12}) shares its formula with three isomers of hexene, each with the double bond between different carbon atoms in the chain, and with ethylbutene: $(C_2H_5)HC{=}CH{-}CH_2{-}CH_3$. Numerous isomers of methylpentene also have the formula C_6H_{12}, each with their methyl group (CH_3) and double bond in different positions.

Properties

Straight-chain, branched, and cyclic alkanes are some of the least reactive hydrocarbons. They are used mainly as fuels and as solvents (dissolving liquids) for other chemicals. The multiple bonds in alkenes and alkynes make them more reactive, since other molecules can break the bonds open and add to the molecule. One type of reaction is polymerization (poh-LIM-uhr-uh-ZAY-shuhn). In polymerization, many thousands of alkenes join together by opening their double bonds and using the spare bonds to form enormous chains. In this way, ethene molecules link up to form polyethylene.

Aromatic hydrocarbons react with a variety of substances to produce useful starting materials for making drugs, dyes, and plastics, among many other things. Aromatics also improve the performance of gasoline fuels.

A United Nations official checking hydrocarbon-containing weapons after the Gulf War (1990–1991).

LOOK CLOSER: Naming Systems

Because of the enormous range of possible groupings of atoms in hydrocarbons, scientists use a naming system that describes the structure of the molecule.

Root	No. Carbons	Ending	Meaning
meth-	1	-ane	all single bonds
eth-	2	-ene	one C=C bond
prop-	3	-diene	two C=C bonds
but-	4	-yl	branching group
pent-	5		
hex-	6	**Prefix**	**Meaning**
hept-	7	cyclo-	ring
oct-	8	poly-	many

Using this system, the name butane (BYOO-tayn) indicates a four-carbon chain that contains only single carbon–carbon bonds, whereas butene (BYOO-teen) is a four-carbon chain with one double carbon–carbon bond, and butadiene (BYOO-tuh-DY-een) is a four-carbon chain with two double carbon–carbon bonds.

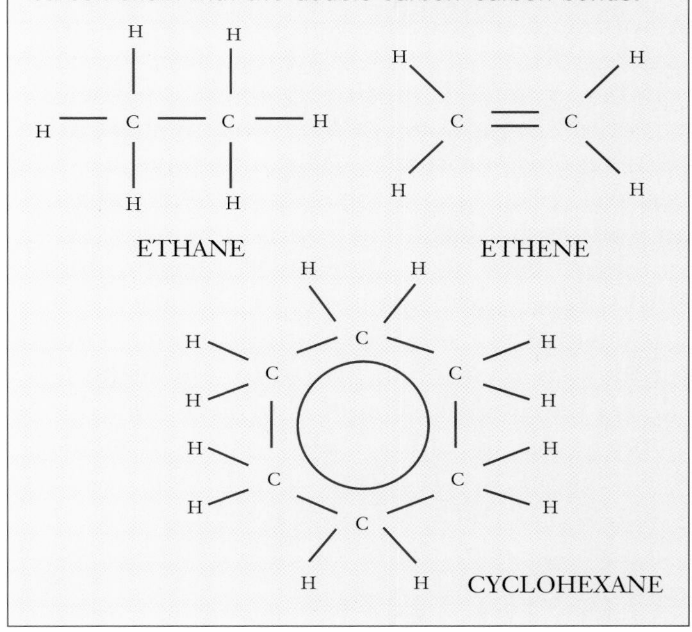

CHECK THESE OUT!

✔CARBOHYDRATE ✔ISOMER ✔ORGANIC CHEMISTRY

Hydrogen

The simplest and lightest of the elements

The first element to form after the big bang (the explosion from which scientists believe the Universe originated) was hydrogen, the most abundant element in the Universe. Under normal conditions on Earth, hydrogen exists as diatomic molecules. These are molecules that consist of two atoms bonded together. The symbol for diatomic hydrogen is H_2.

Hydrogen is present in almost all molecules in living organisms and in all the common fuels. It forms compounds (combines) with metals and nonmetals. One of these compounds, water, is vital for life on Earth. Hydrogen can be made in the laboratory by bringing an acid into contact with a reactive metal. Hydrogen has the simplest atom of all the elements. The nucleus at the center of the atom contains a proton. The nucleus is circled by a single electron.

Isotopes

All of the elements have isotopes. Isotopes are different forms of an element that have the same number of protons (positively charged particles) but different numbers of neutrons (uncharged particles) in their nuclei (NOO-klee-eye; centers). Hydrogen is the only element to have an isotope that has no neutrons. The main isotope of hydrogen, sometimes called protium (PROHT-ee-uhm; symbol H or ^{1}H), has a nucleus that is a single proton. Protium accounts for 99.98 percent of all hydrogen. Deuterium (doo-TIR-ee-uhm; symbol D or ^{2}H) is the isotope with nuclei made up of one proton and one neutron. It is the form of hydrogen in heavy water, D_2O, which is used in some types of nuclear reactors. Only 0.02 percent of hydrogen is deuterium. The third form of hydrogen is also the rarest—tritium, symbol T or ^{3}H. Tritium is formed when cosmic rays (high-speed particles entering Earth's atmosphere from deep space) hit nitrogen atoms in the upper atmosphere. It is extremely radioactive (able to give off rays). Its half-life (the time taken for an amount of a radioactive isotope to decay to half of the original amount) of 12.3 years means only a trace of tritium builds up in the atmosphere.

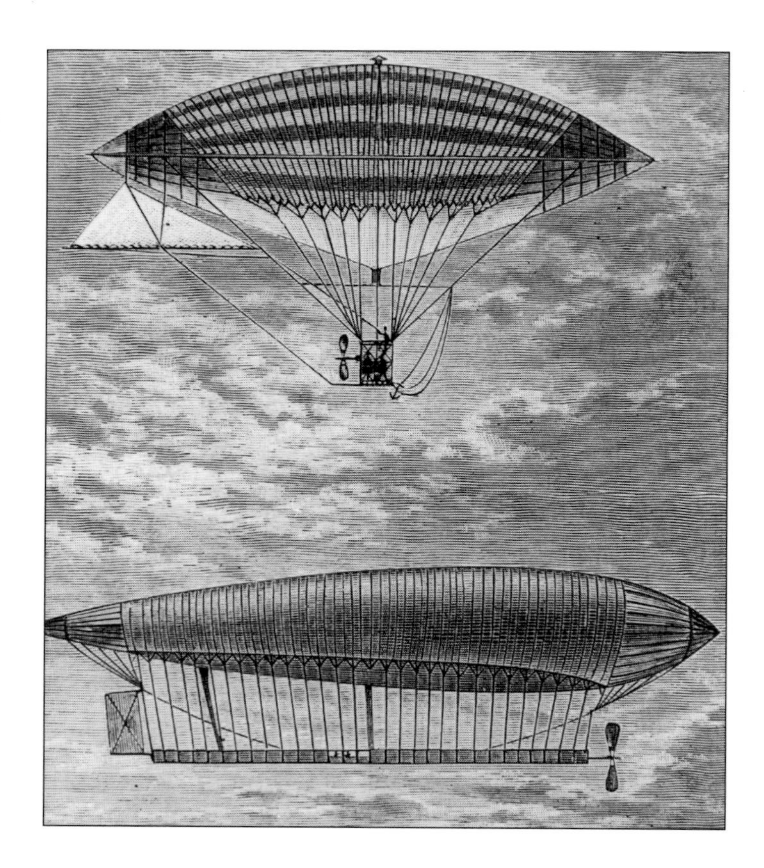

These French airships from the 19th century relied on hydrogen to be able to float in the air.

HIGHLIGHTS

- The three isotopes of hydrogen are: protium, deuterium, and tritium.
- Hydrogen is produced industrially by treating hydrocarbons with steam.

Hydrogen compounds

While water is the most well-known hydrogen compound, many other familiar materials are also compounds of hydrogen. Natural gas is mainly methane, CH_4. Methane is the simplest of the hydrocarbons, which are carbon- and hydrogen-

LOOK CLOSER

Ancestor of the Elements

Scientists believe the Universe began around 12 billion years ago. At first, all the matter in the Universe was crammed into one incredibly hot and dense mass. Suddenly, this mass started to expand at a phenomenal rate. Scientists call this moment the big bang. Protons, neutrons, and electrons—the subatomic particles that make up all atoms—formed within three seconds of the big bang. Because protons are hydrogen nuclei, it can be said that hydrogen, the first element, formed during this period. The Universe was still incredibly hot at the time. It was so hot that electrons and protons would not stick together in atoms. For around eight minutes after the big bang, the Universe behaved like an immense fusion reactor, producing nuclei of helium with two protons and two neutrons each. Within this short period, one-quarter of the mass of the Universe turned into helium. Pockets of hydrogen and helium formed into stars as the Universe continued to expand. Even now, almost two-thirds of the mass of the Universe is hydrogen.

containing compounds. Crude oil is a mixture of much more complex hydrocarbons. Ammonia, NH_3, and hydrogen peroxide, H_2O_2, are used in household products. Hydrogen sulfide, H_2S, is a poisonous gas. Hydrocyanic (HY-DROH-sy-AN-ik) acid, HCN, is also a deadly poison. All of these are combinations of hydrogen and nonmetals.

Acids are an important group of hydrogen compounds. The hydrogen ion, H^+, gives an acid its acidity in water. Important acids include sulfuric acid, H_2SO_4, nitric acid, HNO_3, and hydrochloric acid, HCl. Many naturally occurring acids, such as ethanoic, citric, and tartaric acids, contain the carboxylic (kahr-BAHKS-il-ik) acid group -COOH.

Hydrogen in industry

Hydrogen is manufactured from natural hydrocarbons in a process called steam reforming. First, the hydrocarbon and steam are heated to 1650°F (900°C) with a nickel catalyst (KA-tuhl-uhst; a substance that changes the rate of a chemical reaction without itself being changed). In the case of methane, the equation for the first stage is:

$$CH_4 + H_2O \rightarrow CO + 3H_2.$$

Next, the mixture is cooled to 660°F (350°C), when carbon reacts with more steam to make carbon dioxide and more hydrogen:

$$CO + H_2O \rightarrow CO_2 + H_2.$$

The carbon dioxide that is made is removed.

The biggest use for hydrogen is in the Haber (HAH-buhr) process for making ammonia. Hydrogen and nitrogen react together at around 950°F (510°C) and 200 atmospheres of pressure in the presence of an iron catalyst:

$$N_2 + 3H_2 \rightarrow 2NH_3.$$

Ammonia is an important raw material for fertilizers, dyes, and explosives. Hydrogen is used to convert (change) vegetable oils into edible fats.

Hydrogen as a fuel

Liquid hydrogen is used as a rocket fuel. When it burns, it produces water, so it is less harmful to the environment than fuels such as gasoline and diesel, which produce harmful oxides of carbon and nitrogen when they burn. Hydrogen can also power modified automobile engines. Hydrogen and oxygen are converted into water by fuel cells to make electricity. Fuel cells are more efficient than internal combustion engines because none of the chemical energy is wasted as heat.

CHECK THESE OUT!
✔ACID AND BASE ✔ELEMENT
✔HYDROCARBON ✔ISOTOPE ✔OXIDATION

Hydrology

The science of water and its distribution and circulation around Earth

The study of how water exists and how it is transported around Earth is called hydrology (hy-DRAH-luh-jee). Much of Earth is covered by water. Most of the water is visible on the surface; some of it (groundwater) is hidden within the rocks. Nearly all of the water is constantly moving between oceans, rivers, clouds, and living organisms (AWR-guh-NIH-zuhmz). A process called precipitation (prih-SIH-puh-TAY-shuhn), which includes rainfall, hail, dew, and snow, constantly returns water vapor from the atmosphere into surface water. Another process, called evaporation (ih-VA-puh-RAY-shuhn), makes water vapor rise up into the sky.

Hydrologists (scientists who study water) investigate the effects that people have on water supplies and distribution. Hydrologists often advise how to minimize the effects of engineering projects such as highways and hydroelectric power plants. They may also help restore rivers and waterways that have been affected by human activities.

Humans live on the land and tend to view Earth as though it were a huge island surrounded by a relatively unimportant sea. The reverse is true, however. The oceans take up 70 percent of Earth's surface and hold 97 percent of all the water on the planet. Most of the remaining water is frozen in ice caps and glaciers. Only a tiny proportion of water (less than one-hundredth of one percent) exists in the form of fresh water such as inland streams, marshes, and lakes.

HIGHLIGHTS

- The water (hydrologic) cycle explains how surface water and groundwater are constantly recycled through the atmosphere by processes called evaporation and precipitation.
- The oceans hold more than 97 percent of all the water on Earth; freshwater sources, such as rivers, hold only about one-hundredth of one percent.
- Some human activities pollute surface water and groundwater or disrupt the water cycle. This has a harmful effect on the environment.

Water is essential to life on Earth. It has been estimated that a typical person drinks around 16,000 gallons (60,000 liters) of water in their lifetime. In developed countries, each person uses about 69 gallons (261 liters) of water per day, including all the water used for washing and so on. Water is constantly being recycled in a process called the water (or hydrologic) cycle. However, although water is constantly circulating between the oceans and the atmosphere, it takes longer for some types of water to be recycled than others. For example, water usually stays in rivers for an average of about two weeks, in oceans up to 4,000 years, and hidden within rock strata (STRAH-tuh; layers) as groundwater for anything up to 10,000 years.

Floods are a natural extreme of the water cycle.

Surface water

Water is most obvious in the form of surface water held in the rivers, lakes, oceans, glaciers, and marshes on Earth's surface. As surface water moves so easily, it plays a particularly important role in the water cycle, in the processes of erosion and weathering that break down rocks and soil, and in providing water to living organisms. The vast mass of the ocean warms up and cools down very slowly and helps to even out sudden changes in Earth's climate.

Most of the water that people use each day comes from surface water supplies. Growing populations in many parts of the world have placed huge demands on the water supply system, which can easily become polluted and carry dangerous diseases such as cholera (KAH-luh-ruh; a disease that affects the stomach and intestine). Pesticides used on farmland may leak into rivers and seas to kill fish. Sulfur dioxide produced by emissions from power plant smokestacks is soaked up by rain to form sulfuric acid. The acid is carried by the wind and may fall hundreds of miles away from the power plant in the form of acid rain.

Groundwater

Only around 0.6 percent of Earth's water is buried beneath the ground, but given how much water there is on Earth altogether, this represents a vast underground supply. Groundwater exists in underground reservoirs called aquifers (A-kwuh-fuhrs) at a natural level beneath Earth's surface called the water table. An aquifer is a layer of porous (POHR-uhs; water-holding) material such as chalk, sand, or gravel, sandwiched between nonporous strata such as clay.

Groundwater can be extracted (taken out) from Earth by sinking wells and boreholes into aquifers and then pumping water to the surface. Groundwater may be under enough pressure for it to rise to the surface when a borehole is put down into an aquifer.

Just like surface water, groundwater supplies can also be damaged by human activities. Highways and building foundations, for example, may cut through and damage aquifers. In addition, chemical pollution may leak into the underground aquifers and remain there for many years. Taking too much water from an aquifer causes the water table to fall and may kill nearby plants that also depend on the underground supply. Human misuse of groundwater is very serious because it can take up to 10,000 years to recharge an aquifer.

LOOK CLOSER

The Water Cycle

The water (hydrologic) cycle is driven by the twin processes of evaporation and precipitation. Evaporation lifts water from Earth into the sky; precipitation carries it back down to Earth. Rainfall is just one of a number of different types of precipitation. Other types include dew, frost, fog, drizzle, rain, sleet, and snow. Human activity can interfere with the water cycle. Damming and diverting rivers interferes with the flow of sediments (SEH-duh-muhnts; material that settles to the bottom) from the rivers into the seas and can harm fish, such as salmon, that swim between the two. Deforestation (cutting down trees) and other destruction of vegetation causes soil to be washed away more easily and makes it harder to grow crops. It also interferes with the water cycle in places such as the rain forests where the trees carefully regulate evaporation and precipitation.

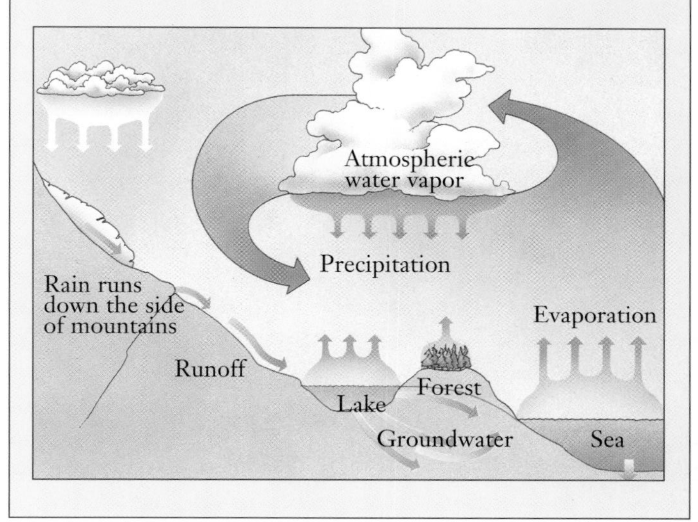

CHECK THESE OUT!

✔GLACIER ✔GROUNDWATER ✔ICE
✔LAKE ✔OCEAN ✔RAIN, SLEET, AND SNOW
✔RIVER ✔WATER

Hydrothermal Vent

A volcanic opening on the ocean floor that releases heated, mineral-rich water

The interior of Earth is very hot. Below Earth's crust, the rock is hot. It becomes molten when it has risen very near to the surface in a volcanic pipe. At some places on the ocean floor, seawater can seep through cracks in Earth's crust.

HIGHLIGHTS

- Ocean water can seep down through cracks in the ocean floor until it reaches the molten rock below.
- The heat forces the water up again, under pressure, and it emerges from an opening called a hydrothermal (hot water) vent.
- The water contains minerals from the lavas just below Earth's surface, which have brought chemicals from much deeper down. They come out of solution and form dramatic structures, such as mounds and chimneys.
- The main minerals present are sulfides, which provide energy for organisms called archaeobacteria.
- The heated water from a hydrothermal vent and the presence of the archaeobacteria encourage the growth of other creatures such as giant clams, mussels, and crabs.

When the water reaches the molten magma, it is heated and forced back up to the surface. The openings through which the hot water emerges are called hydrothermal vents. *Hydrothermal* means "of heated water."

Rather like small volcanoes that expel clouds of ash and gas into the atmosphere, hydrothermal vents spew hot water, rich in minerals, into the ocean. The cold ocean water cools the emerging hot water, and the minerals present come out of solution. These minerals form dramatic structural shapes, such as mounds and chimneys,

Organisms that live near hydrothermal vents, such as these giant tube worms, have a body chemistry that relies on sulfur, rather than oxygen, to produce energy.

around the vents on the ocean floor. The vents occur thousands of feet deep in the water, along ridges that form the boundaries between the tectonic plates that make up Earth's surface.

In the Pacific Ocean, vents have been discovered near the equator at the Galápagos Rift, the East Pacific Rise, and at the northern Juan de Fuca Ridge. In the North Atlantic, the vents occur in the Mid-Atlantic Ridge.

Temperatures in the vent water have been recorded from 45°F (7°C) to as high as 750°F (400°C). The water stays liquid above its normal boiling point (212°F or 100°C) because it is under intense pressure. It is also slightly acidic. This acidity and the water's high temperature keep the minerals dissolved until the water emerges into the cold ocean.

As it seeps through Earth's crust, seawater gives up some substances and takes others from the molten rock. One of the most common compounds to emerge is hydrogen sulfide, the gas that is also produced by rotten eggs. There are other sulfide compounds, including those of iron, zinc, manganese, and copper.

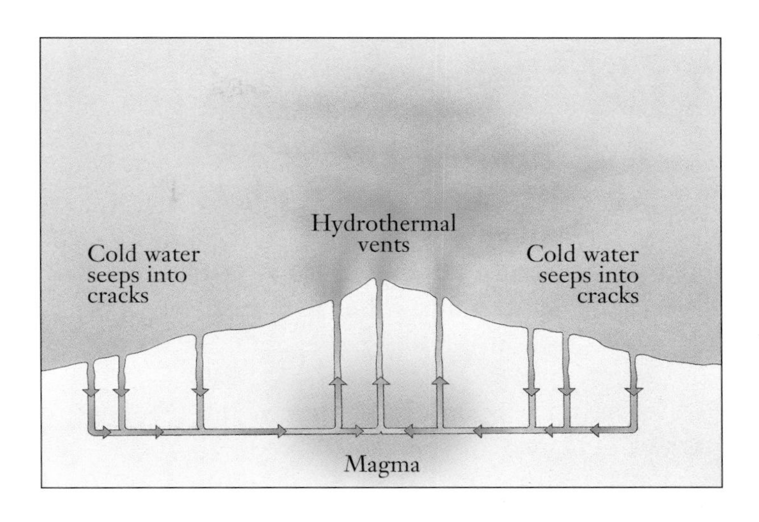

Cold water is drawn into cracks in the ocean floor, then heated and forced out of hydrothermal vents.

When the vent spews out black iron sulfide from its chimney, it is called a black smoker. The chimney can be more than 33 feet (10 m) high and 13 feet (4 m) wide. There are also vents called white smokers. The water emerging from these vents contains barium minerals.

DISCOVERERS

Finding the Galápagos Rift Vents

In February 1977, a team led by Robert Ballard of Woods Hole Oceanographic Institution and Jack Corliss of Oregon State University, began searching the deep ocean on the Galápagos Rift, off the coast of Ecuador. Previous observers had noted odd temperature rises, which they called temperature spikes, in the deep water in this area. The team used an underwater camera sled called ANGUS. The camera shot thousands of photographs of the ocean floor. A few photographs showed clams and mussels in cloudy water. Corliss suspected that the temperature spikes were connected with the presence of these shellfish. On February 19, 1977, he and a colleague got aboard a tiny submersible named *Alvin* and descended 9,200 feet (2,800 m) to the ocean floor. After searching for some time, the scientists found an area crowded with clusters of giant clams and tube worms. The water was 10 to 15 degrees warmer than the surrounding ocean water and it seemed to shimmer. It was a hot spring from a hydrothermal vent. During the four weeks of the expedition, the team discovered five hot springs in the Galápagos Rift.

Food sources

The heated water close to hydrothermal vents has resulted in the development of some unique life-forms. Tiny, single-celled, bacterialike organisms called archaeobacteria (AHR-kee-oh-bak-TIHR-ee-uh) form the base of the food chain at hydrothermal vents. These organisms make their food by using the energy from chemical reactions involving vent fluids, particularly those containing sulfides. In turn, other organisms feed on the archaeobacteria. However, the thick-plumed rift worm, which is found at the Galápagos Rift, has no digestive system of its own. Instead, it is a host to bacteria that live inside its body and provide it with food. Other organisms found at the Galápagos Rift include giant clams, mussels, and crabs.

CHECK THESE OUT!
✔OCEAN ✔PLATE TECTONICS ✔VOLCANO

Ice

The solid form of water

Water is the only common substance on Earth that is familiar in each of its three forms: solid, liquid, and gas. Ice is water in its solid form. Ice has a number of unusual properties that affect Earth's climate, its landscapes, and people's everyday lives.

Water freezes (solidifies) to become ice when the temperature falls below 32°F (0°C) at standard air pressure. Water is made up of molecules of two atoms of hydrogen combined with one atom of oxygen, to form the compound H_2O. As water cools, the molecules start to move more slowly. As water freezes, the molecules become fixed in an arrangement called a crystal.

Hoarfrost happens when damp air cools, allowing ice crystals to form in clusters on objects such as trees.

HIGHLIGHTS

- Ice is the solid form of water. Water freezes to form ice when the temperature falls below 32°F (0°C) at standard air pressure.
- The density of ice is less than water; therefore, water expands as it freezes.
- The freezing point of water gets lower as the pressure applied to it increases.
- Snowflakes are hexagonal (six-sided) crystals of ice. A hailstone is a more compact mass of ice made up of many different crystals.

Unusual properties of ice

When water molecules form ice crystals, the distance between the molecules increases. They become less dense (more widely spaced) and therefore take up more room. Water expands by 9 percent as it freezes. It is this that causes frozen water pipes to burst in winter. It also means that ice, being less dense than water, floats in water, with one-tenth of its mass below the surface. Because ice is lighter than water, oceans and lakes do not freeze from the bottom up. Instead, ice forms at the surface, and the deeper water below is protected from freezing by the surface layer. This fact is crucial to the survival of all types of animals that live in water.

Another important property of water is that its freezing point becomes lower as the pressure on it increases. Ice will also melt at a lower temperature when under pressure. This property can be shown by hanging a heavy weight on a thin wire laid over a block of ice. Under the pressure of the wire, the ice melts, and the wire slowly sinks through the block. The slipperiness of icy roads is due to this unusual property of water. Under pressure from the weight of heavy cars, the surface ice melts, making roads dangerously slippery. Glaciers are large masses of ice that flow slowly downhill for the same reason. The great weight of the ice pressing down melts the ice at the bottom of the glacier, which is in contact with the rocks beneath. This allows the mass of the glacier to slip forward over the rock on a thin film of water. Heavy objects left on the surface of thick ice for long periods have been lost forever because they sank to the depths.

Snow, frost, and hail

Snowflakes are single crystals of ice. They are always hexagonal (six-sided). Depending on the conditions in which they form, snow and frost crystals can be many different shapes, from simple or complex stars to needles and hollow columns, or a combination of these. It is often said that no two snowflakes are exactly the same.

Snow and frost are formed from water in its gas form, water vapor. Hail is ice formed from liquid water and is made up of a mass of many different crystals. As ice forms, its molecules become fixed in layers in a crystal structure called a lattice (LA-tuhs). This structure affects the way in which ice shears (breaks) when it is put under pressure. Under a strong enough sideways force, each layer of ice crystals slides over the layers above and below it, breaking and forming new bonds in the lattice structure.

Snow reflects up to 90 percent of the light falling on it, but glacier ice reflects much less light. Both snow and ice absorb almost all of the Sun's infrared rays. When snow and glacier ice are dry, radio waves pass through them relatively easily. Radar can therefore be used to measure the depth of dry glaciers, even when they are several miles thick.

EVERYDAY SCIENCE

Freezing Food

Water expands as it solidifies, which makes freezing some kinds of foods difficult. The cell walls of soft, moist fruits such as raspberries and strawberries, for example, are often broken as the water they contain expands during freezing. This causes the fruit to become mushy when it is thawed.

In certain conditions, when little water vapor is present in the air, ice and snow can move directly from their solid form to a vapor without first melting to become liquid. This unusual event, called sublimation (SUH-bluh-MAY-shuhn), is used when foods such as coffee granules (shown below) are freeze-dried. The food is first frozen and then exposed to a vacuum (VA-kyoom; empty space). The water content in the food is almost all removed as vapor. The dry food contains only about 2 percent water.

CHECK THESE OUT!

✔CRYSTAL ✔GLACIER ✔WATER

Ice Age

Cold climate spell during which glacial ice spreads over land that is normally ice-free

An ice age is a time of extremely cold weather that may last for thousands of years. There have been at least seven ice ages during Earth's 4.6-billion-year history. Glaciers and ice sheets spread during ice ages. During an ice age (glacial period), the climate swings back and forth many times between periods of intense cold and milder interglacial episodes. Scientists do not completely understand why Earth's climate changes in this way. Ice ages have a great effect on the land. All the plants are killed off as glaciers advance, and birds and animals are forced to migrate to warmer places to survive.

Earth has been in the grip of an ice age, called the Quaternary ice age, for the last two million years. The last extremely cold period ended about 12,000 years ago. Since then, the ice sheets and glaciers have shrunk back. It is possible that Earth is currently in an interglacial time and that the extremely cold weather may return. Temperatures are no warmer now than in a typical interglacial period. Ice sheets may return within the next 20,000 to 40,000 years, despite the present threat of global warming, which is mainly the result of human activity.

HIGHLIGHTS

- There have been at least seven episodes of extreme cold in Earth's history. These episodes are called ice ages.
- At present, Earth is in a warm interglacial interval within the Quaternary ice age. This has lasted about 10,000 years. Earth is due to enter another glacial deep freeze in around 20,000 to 40,000 years' time.
- Ice ages seem to be caused by the varying output of the Sun's heat and the movement of Earth's crustal plates, which determine ocean circulation and climate patterns as well as the position of the continents relative to the poles.
- It is so cold during ice ages that ocean surfaces may freeze over.
- The Ordovician ice age (which ended about 440 million years ago) was probably responsible for the widespread extinction of many creatures, especially those living in the sea.

A very young mammoth that was first preserved in ice in Siberia, Russia, around 10,000 years ago.

Evidence of ice ages

When an ice age happens, more snow falls in the polar regions than melts away. The climate is so cold that the ocean surface may freeze. Snow piles up each year, and the heat of the Sun is reflected from the white surface. The thickening layers of snow are compressed and ice begins to form deep down. Eventually, the weight of ice on the land becomes so great that Earth's crust may be pushed down. Also, so much water gets locked away as ice that the sea level falls.

Ice forms in crystals and can move slowly under pressure. The weight of growing ice sheets and glaciers causes them to move and flow outward. As they move, the land surface is scratched and eroded. Bits of loose rock caught up in the bottom of the ice will scratch the underlying rock, acting like the grains in a sheet of sandpaper. This grinding process is abrasion. The landscape is changed completely by this ice movement. River valleys are made wider and deeper and take on a U-shape. Rock debris (duh-BREE; loose particles) is carried by the ice and finally dumped when the ice melts to form large mounds called moraines. Melting ice sheets release huge volumes of water that make powerful rivers carrying mud, sand, gravel, and boulders, which erode deep channels. This fluvio-glacial sediment (sediment carried in rivers coming from the ice) changes the landscape on which it is deposited. As the ice sheets melt, so the land—which was previously weighed down by the ice—rises up. Even today, Scandinavia and the Hudson Bay area of Canada are rising at about ⅓ inch (1 cm) per year. This rise is called isostatic (EYE-suh-STAT-ik) recovery. In areas near the coast, the shorelines are lifted up and raised beaches form high above the new sea level.

LOOK CLOSER

Last Ice Age

The last great advance of the ice sheets reached its maximum around 18,000 years ago. In North America, the snow and ice piled up to form a vast sheet, estimated to have been around 9,800 feet (2,940 m) thick and covering most of Canada. The southern margin of the ice sheet reached south of the U.S. border, especially in the Great Lakes region. Beyond the ice, the ground was permanently frozen (permafrost) all year for some distance to the south. Only small tough herbs, mosses, and lichens (LY-kuhnz) grew in patches on the barren stony surface. Farther south, there was coniferous forest and grassland that fed migrating herds of bison, caribou (a type of deer), mammoths, and horses.

In certain places, the climate was so dry that finely ground glacial rock debris was blown around by the wind to form cold desertlike dunes of sand and loess (LOH-EHS; deposit made of silt-sized grains). When the ice melted, vast rivers carried away glacial sand, gravel, and mud. Lakes formed and sometimes burst their banks to flood over the surrounding landscapes, as in the channeled scablands of Washington state.

Previous ice ages

Geologists (scientists who study the structure and history of rocks) have found evidence for at least six previous ice ages. Tillites are sedimentary rocks formed by ice ages. They are rocks made of a jumble of mud, sand, and pebbles and have been found in strata (STRAH-tuh; rock layers) as old as the Precambrian (before 570 million years ago).

During the Precambrian, there may have been three separate ice ages at 2.7 billion, 2.3 billion, and 900 million years ago. Later ice ages happened at the end of the Ordovician period (about 440 million years ago), the end of the Carboniferous period (300 million years ago), and finally the Quaternary ice age, which began about 1.6 million years ago.

The Ordovician ice age is well represented by tillites and glacial scratches (striations) on rocks in North Africa, which was near the South Pole 450 million years ago. This ice age is thought to have been the cause of a widespread extinction of many creatures, especially those living in the sea. The Carboniferous ice age is proved by tillites in India, southern Africa, South America, Antarctica, and Australia. These countries were then joined together in a large continent called Gondwana.

The Quaternary ice age

The world's climate started cooling at least 30 million years ago. Antarctic glaciers started flowing down to sea level, but the glaciers in the northern hemisphere did not develop until about 1.6 million years ago. Each glacial episode, when the glaciers increase in size and advance, tends to remove evidence of an earlier advance. For this reason, geologists find it difficult to work out how many advances and retreats there may have been, although there is now general agreement on six ice ages. Evidence from sediment cores taken on the deep sea bed have given accurate details of climate change and the coming and going of ice sheets.

Causes of ice ages

The climate of Earth is never the same for very long. Over millions of years many significant changes may happen. This can be because of changes in the heat that is given out by the Sun, slight shifts of Earth on its axis, and the changes in the shape and size of the continents. Serbian astronomer Milutin Milankovitch (1897–1958)

DISCOVERERS

Changing Views of Ice Ages

Until well into the 19th century, few people had any idea that glacial ice could spread beyond the poles. The fossil remains of animals such as mammoth, rhinoceros, and hyena in northern Europe were explained by the biblical flood. It was thought that the animals had been carried north by the flood waters. Even the existing glaciers of the European Alps were not thought to have flowed beyond their present extent.

By the end of the 18th century, some European experts such as Scottish geologist and chemist James Hutton (1726–1797) argued that certain surface deposits called drift and large boulders scattered over parts of northern Europe had been dumped by extensive glaciers in the past. Arguments raged for many years until Swiss geologist Louis Agassiz (1807–1873; above) was able to demonstrate convincingly in the 1830s that glaciation had occurred over vast regions of northern Europe and North America. From his experience of active glaciation in the Swiss Alps, Agassiz could explain how landscape features such as striated and molded rock surfaces, erratic boulders, and moraine deposits could be formed only by glaciation.

Evidence had been found by the 1860s to show that an ice age was not continuously cold but contained significant warm climate phases. Scottish scientist James Croll (1821–1890) also proposed that the regular changes in glacial climates are driven by astronomical cycles. The idea was later developed by Serbian astronomer Milutin Milankovitch (1897–1958) and related to the tilt of the Earth's axis of rotation and orbit around the Sun.

By the 20th century, geologists had worked out a series of some six main glacials with intervening interglacials during the last ice age. However, during the 1970s and 1980s, scientists discovered that the last ice age had many more climate changes and started much longer ago than previously thought.

suggested that astronomical cycles (including periods of change in Earth's axis) might change the world's climate and start an ice age.

There are many probable reasons for the start of an ice age. There must be enough snow falling near the poles, and winds should ideally blow out from the cold regions to spread the low temperature toward lower latitudes. The spread of ice sheets and glaciers can happen only when there is a large landmass near the pole. At many times in the past this has not been the case. The Arctic ocean can freeze over, as it does today, but glaciers cannot spread out unless there is land near the poles, as with the most recent ice age, during which glaciers and ice sheets spread south into Europe and North America. Antarctica is permanently mostly covered with ice sheets, but they can not spread into the surrounding sea.

LOOK CLOSER

Ocean Drilling

Great advances in an understanding of the past have come from the recent Ocean Drilling Project. By drilling into the ocean floor and recovering continuous sediment cores, scientists have been able to obtain a detailed record of changes in sedimentation and ocean water. Analysis of the shell composition of ocean-dwelling microorganisms gives a measure of changes in ocean water composition. This, in turn, is related to the amount of water from melted glaciers that was released into the oceans during interglacial warm phases. These measurements give a much more detailed picture than any previously obtained of climatic changes over the last two million years of the ice age.

CHECK THESE OUT!
✔GEOLOGIC TIMESCALE ✔GLACIER ✔GONDWANA ✔ICE ✔QUATERNARY PERIOD

About 18,000 years ago, the whole of Canada and a strip of the United States was covered in ice.

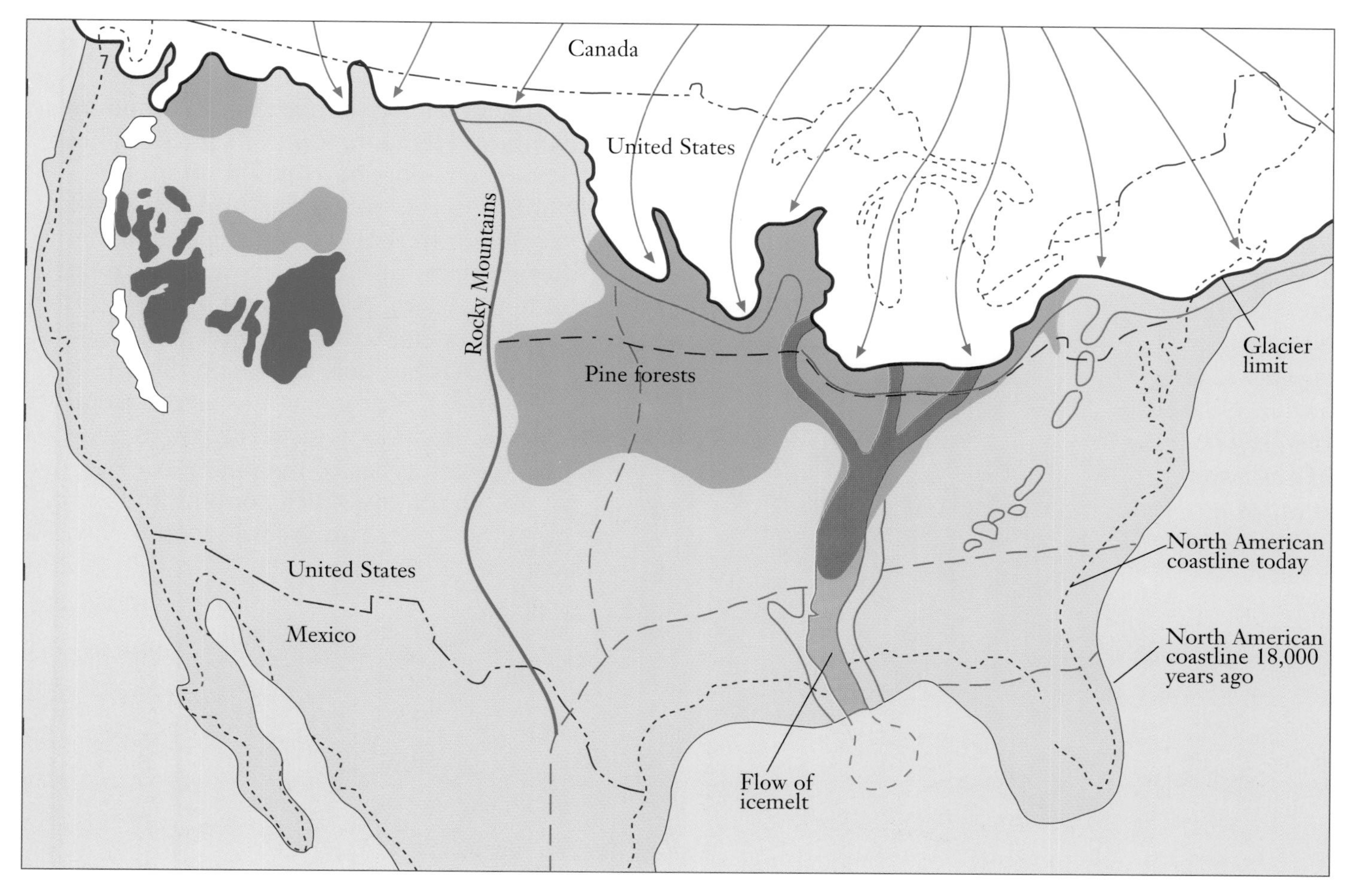

Igneous Rock

Type of rock formed when magma cools and solidifies

HIGHLIGHTS

- Igneous rocks are either intrusive or extrusive.
- Magma is a mixture of compounds of iron, sodium, aluminum, calcium, silicon, oxygen, and potassium.

Much of Earth's crust is made of igneous (IG-nee-uhs) rocks. There are two main types of igneous rock: intrusive and extrusive. Intrusive rocks are formed when magma solidifies below ground; extrusive rocks are created when lava (LAH-vuh) comes onto the surface and cools. Basalt is the most common igneous rock. It is a type of lava that covers most of the ocean floors and many land areas. Tuff is an extrusive volcanic rock made of dust and small fragments of rock from a volcanic explosion. Granite (GRAH-nuht) is an intrusive igneous rock, occuring deep in Earth's crust.

What igneous rocks look like

When molten magma or lava cools, crystals such as quartz (KWAWRTS), feldspar, and mica (MY-kuh) gradually form. If the magma is deep underground, it cools slowly and the crystals have a chance to develop good shapes and sizes. These coarse-grained rocks, especially granite, have a distinctive mosaic (pattern of various colors) of crystals. The crystals in a rock such as basalt are very small and badly shaped because they have cooled so quickly. They are too small to be seen with the naked eye. Sometimes lava cools so quickly that no real crystals are formed, and rocks like obsidian (uhb-SIH-dee-uhn; a natural glass) are created.

A mass of lava and rock debris clogging the vent of a volcano is called a volcanic plug.

What igneous rocks are made of

Igneous rocks are made when magma cools down. Magma contains a mixture of compounds of the common elements found in Earth. These include oxygen, silicon, iron, aluminum, calcium, sodium, potassium, and magnesium. There are different types of magma in different parts of Earth's crust. Each type contains varying proportions of the common elements. A major part of all magmas is silica, or silicon dioxide (SiO_2). Many magmas also contain water. Geologists recognize two main types of magma. Basic magma has a low silica content and makes very runny lava when it comes onto the surface. Acid magma is rich in silica and does not flow. Volcanoes made of acid lava are very explosive because the lava solidifies in the volcanic crater, and a great build-up of pressure is required to force out more lava.

Common extrusive rock formations

Basalt lavas are the most common extrusive igneous rocks. Much of this basalt occurs on the ocean floor, where the tectonic plates are spreading apart at the mid-ocean ridges. As this lava erupts, a skin immediately forms around the lava masses and stretches like a huge pillow as more lava is pushed out. These pillow lavas are typical of underwater eruptions.

Much runny basalt has flooded out onto the continents. The Columbia Plateau basalts in Oregon and Washington began pouring out 17 million years ago. Lavas that flow quickly often have smooth surfaces, or they may be ropey and are called pahoehoe (pa-HOH-ee-HOH-ee). Other slower-flowing lavas form blocks and lumps on the surface and are called aa (ah-ah) lavas. Both of these names come from Hawaii, where much of this lava occurs. When the lava cools, it shrinks and cracks. These cracks, called joints, often form amazing patterns.

A terrifying type of eruption occurs when a cloud of gas mixed with red-hot lava droplets flows down the volcano slopes at over 125 miles per hour (200 km/h). This flow, called a pyroclastic (PY-roh-KLAS-tik) flow, devastates everything in its path and finally settles out to form a welded tuff, with all its small lava and rock fragments literally welded together by the heat of the flow. Acid lavas form steep-sided volcanoes because the lava does not flow easily.

Structures formed by intrusive rocks

It is easy to see a volcano and watch it forming, but it is impossible to witness the large masses of igneous rock that form underground when magma cools. Geologists have to rely on the effects of weathering and erosion to see underground rock formations. The largest igneous rock masses are called batholiths (BA-thuh-liths). These are huge rock features that may cover many tens of square miles. They originate deep in Earth's crust, and the magma gradually seeps upward, melting and pushing its way through other rocks. Large fragments of the invaded rock (called country rock) are often caught up in the edges of the batholith rock.

There are two very common small-scale intrusive structures. Cracks form when Earth's crust stretches. These cracks are filled in from below by igneous rock. Such vertical sheets of rock are called dykes and are often made of dolerite (DAH-luh-ryt). This rock is closely related to basalt but has slightly larger crystals. Dykes often occur in great numbers, as in New England. Horizontal sheets of igneous rock are called sills. These follow the local rock patterns and do not cut across them as dykes do.

LOOK CLOSER

Landscapes

In the Sierra Nevada (see below), there is a mass of intrusive igneous rock called a batholith. It was formed when dinosaurs roamed the land. The granite forming the batholith called Half Dome and El Capitan has been studied for many years and is a favorite place for rock climbing. The whole batholith is about 400 miles (650 km) long by 60 miles (100 km) wide and is made up of a number of smaller rock masses. Originally, it was intruded (magma that solidified) deep in Earth's crust and at least 6 miles (10 km) of rock has been removed by erosion, so the granite can now be seen. During the last ice age over two million years ago, the Yosemite valley was carved out by glaciers, which have left scratches in the rock as evidence of their movement.

CHECK THESE OUT!
✔LANDFORM ✔MAGMA ✔METAMORPHIC ROCK ✔ROCK ✔SEDIMENTARY ROCK ✔VOLCANO

Indian Ocean

Earth's third largest ocean, which lies broadly south of India

The world's third largest ocean is the Indian Ocean. Only the Pacific and Atlantic Oceans are bigger. The Indian Ocean has several features that make it different from the Pacific and Atlantic. It is landlocked in the north, so it does not extend into the colder northern regions. More unusual is the fact that many of the Indian Ocean's currents change direction, reversing twice each year. They do so in response to tropical winds that bring seasonal heavy rains called monsoons to India and southern Asia.

Area and coastline

The Indian Ocean is edged by a coastline that stretches for 40,000 miles (64,000 km). It runs from India along the Bay of Bengal, down through the islands of Indonesia, along the west coast of Australia, past Antarctica, up to Africa, along the Arabian peninsula, across the Persian Gulf, and back to India. These boundaries enclose an expanse of 28.4 million square miles (73.4 million sq km) of ocean surface—about one-fifth of the planet's total ocean surface.

The Indian Ocean has an average depth of 12,700 feet (3,850 m). A number of smaller seas and other stretches of water are considered part of it, including the Arabian, Java, Red, and Timor Seas. In some areas, undersea mountains and plateaus (pla-TOHZ; flat areas) rise out of the water to form islands, including Madagascar, Sri Lanka, and the Seychelles.

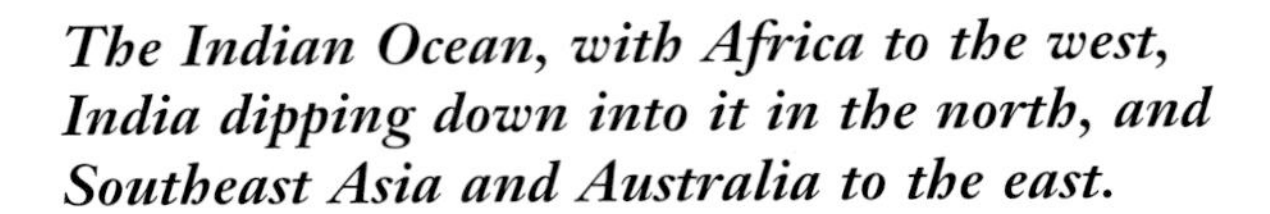

The Indian Ocean, with Africa to the west, India dipping down into it in the north, and Southeast Asia and Australia to the east.

HIGHLIGHTS

- The Indian Ocean is the world's third largest ocean. It occupies about one-fifth of the world's total ocean surface.
- The Indian Ocean was formed about 100 million years ago by the breakup of the ancient supercontinent of Gondwana.
- North of the equator, Indian Ocean currents reverse their direction twice a year in response to monsoon winds.
- The floor of the Indian Ocean contains a number of dramatic landscape features, including sheer ridges, high plateaus, and deep trenches.

How the Indian Ocean was formed

The Indian Ocean is younger than the Atlantic and Pacific. Evidence suggests that it formed during the last 100 million years. The Atlantic began to split apart around 110 million years ago. Broadly speaking, the ocean was created by movement of the giant plates, called tectonic plates, that make up Earth's crust and part of the upper mantle. These plates may carry both dry land and ocean. Around 135 million years ago, the huge ancient continent of Gondwana slowly broke up. The plate bearing India gradually drifted northward to collide with the plate bearing Asia.

Ocean currents

The Indian Ocean's currents reverse direction twice a year because of changing wind patterns in the region. In winter, the northeast monsoon brings strong winds that push currents in a westerly direction. The currents flow toward Africa and then swing south until they reach the equator, where they swing back to the east. During summer, the southwest monsoon creates the opposite current. South of the equator, the prevailing currents flow west to east throughout the year.

Features of the ocean floor

If the Indian Ocean were drained of its water, it would be a rugged landscape of high, steep ridges towering over deep basins and yawning trenches. One of its most spectacular features is the mid-ocean ridge. This sheer ridge runs southward from the Gulf of Aden and then forks like an upside-down Y. One arm runs southwest below the southern tip of Africa; the other curves southeast. The ridge follows the boundary where several of Earth's tectonic plates meet. Seismic (SYZ-mik) activity (earthquakes and volcanic eruptions) are common along plate boundaries, where they create new crust.

Most of the margins of the Indian Ocean are free of seismic activity. However, volcanoes and earthquakes occur in the east, especially around the island of Sumatra, along another plate boundary where ocean crust is being created. This seismic activity is most concentrated near the Sunda Trench, the Indian Ocean's deepest trench, which drops to 24,600 feet (7,455 m).

LOOK CLOSER

Aseismic Ridges

Ocean ridges and plateaus that may have formed as a result of volcanic activity but are no longer active are called aseismic (AY-SYZ-mik) ridges. Several of these ridges are found in the Indian Ocean. The best-known is Ninety East Ridge. This high ridge runs north-south along the ocean floor in a nearly straight line for 3,100 miles (5,000 km). Its crest towers as high as 12,000 feet (3,658 m) above the ocean floor. Scientists believe that Ninety East Ridge was formed as a result of the tectonic plate movements that set India drifting northward to collide with the continent of Asia.

The Chagos Laccadive Plateau is another major aseismic feature. Situated off the west coast of India, it rises above the ocean surface in several places, forming the Maldive and Laccadive Islands. Like the Ninety East Ridge, it is thought to have formed as India drifted north to collide with Asia.

Natural resources

Two-fifths of the world's offshore petroleum mining takes place in the Indian Ocean. Most of the ocean's other resources remain largely untapped. Large quantities of natural gas exist, but little is mined. Only about one percent of the world's natural gas comes from the region.

Nodules of manganese, a hard metallic element, are another valuable resource found on the ocean floor. These grapefruit-sized lumps form at depths of 2 to 3 miles (3 to 5 km). They may contain iron, nickel, cobalt, and copper as well as manganese. Fortunately for the wildlife of the Indian Ocean, the high cost of mining and processing the nodules makes extraction too expensive. Conflicting claims by the 35 nations that border the Indian Ocean also limit the exploitation of its natural resources.

CHECK THESE OUT!
✔GONDWANA ✔MONSOON ✔PLATE TECTONICS

Infrared Radiation

Electromagnetic radiation with wavelengths longer than those of visible light but shorter than 1 mm

HIGHLIGHTS

- Infrared is invisible radiation with wavelengths between 730 nm and 1 mm.
- Infrared waves have less energy than visible light and so can be produced by cooler objects.
- Infrared waves are the radiation sensed as heat.
- All warm objects produce infrared radiation, which tends to flow from hot objects to cold ones, warming them up.

Visible light has colors ranging from red to violet. Light waves of each color have different wavelengths and frequencies (number of waves per second) from the others. Visible light is one part of a wider range of radiation, including radio waves and ultraviolet radiation, that forms the electromagnetic spectrum. Electromagnetic waves with wavelengths slightly longer than red light make up the infrared part of this spectrum. Infrared rays carry less energy than visible light. They can be produced by objects not hot enough to glow with visible light, but they can carry heat from one object to another.

Properties of infrared

Infrared waves have wavelengths between 730 nm (nanometers; 1 nanometer is one-billionth of a meter) and 1 mm. They were first recorded in 1800 by English astronomer William Herschel (1738–1822). Herschel was measuring the amount of heat energy carried by different colors of sunlight. He passed a ray of white sunlight through a prism (PRIH-zuhm; shaped glass), which split it into different colors, and then used a thermometer to measure the temperature of each region. When he moved the thermometer into the region inside the red end of the spectrum (into the infrared region), the temperature suddenly rose. Today's scientists know that nearly half the Sun's energy is released into space as infrared radiation.

Infrared waves are a type of electromagnetic radiation. They can move through a vacuum (VA-kyoom; empty space)

This infrared satellite image of Hong Kong shows green vegetation as red, urban areas as a light blue or gray color, and water as black.

and transfer heat between objects by radiation (other types of heat transfer need to pass through a material). All warm objects emit infrared radiation. Most materials also absorb infrared energy. Radiation tends to transfer energy from hotter objects to colder ones.

Some materials called insulators (IN-suh-lay-tuhrz) absorb less infrared than others. Glass, which lets visible light pass through, absorbs infrared radiation. Gas molecules in Earth's atmosphere act in the same way, absorbing most of the Sun's infrared radiation before it reaches the ground. Without this protection, Earth's surface would become too hot to support life.

Uses of infrared

Infrared radiation is used to detect radiation and change it into visual information or data that a computer can analyze. Infrared heat lamps dry ink or paint on production lines and printing presses, and they also provide warmth to areas that cannot be heated easily otherwise.

Because infrared radiation is produced by objects that are not hot enough to glow visibly, it can be used to look at objects that are invisible in ordinary light. However, the usual methods used to capture and record light are not sensitive to infrared, so normal video cameras or photographic films are useless.

Some photographic films have coatings that make them sensitive to infrared. When these films are developed they produce a false-color image of an object, called a thermogram. Electronic thermograms can be made using infrared-sensitive materials that produce an electric current depending on the intensity of the radiation they record. This is then processed and displayed on screen.

Infrared imaging has a wide variety of uses. Weather satellites use it to detect cloud patterns and predict the weather. Remote-sensing satellites can peer through smoke to find the edge of a forest fire or to detect the heat signatures (patterns) of particular crops growing on the ground.

Astronomers use infrared light to reveal information about the Universe hidden in normal light. Detecting infrared radiation from space is difficult because of the heat coming from Earth and the way in which the atmosphere absorbs most of the radiation from space. Infrared telescopes have been built on mountain tops, but the most successful ones have been satellites launched into space. These need to be cooled to very low temperatures to stop their own heat interfering with their measurements.

The same technology is used in warfare to cool the infrared detectors of heat-seeking missiles such as the Sidewinder. This cooling enables the missile to distinguish the engines and also other, cooler parts of a target such as an aircraft. Computer-controlled guidance systems can then direct the missile to its target.

EVERYDAY SCIENCE

Seeing the Invisible

Infrared imaging devices show users with goggles or cameras that produce infrared images in real time. These devices use electronic detectors to detect differences in the amount of infrared radiation from different parts of an object. They then change this information into a visible picture of heat distribution, showing heat differences as different colors or intensities of light.

Infrared imaging was invented for use in military night sights but has found other uses. Police forces use infrared cameras to chase criminals in darkness. Earthquake rescue teams use similar devices to look for survivors buried beneath rubble. Imaging devices are used for finding points of heat loss in buildings. Because changes in materials often affect their heat signatures (particular heat patterns), the same technology is used for geological surveys to identify different types of rocks and for monitoring pollution.

CHECK THESE OUT!

✔ELECTROMAGNETIC SPECTRUM ✔HEAT
✔SPECTROSCOPY ✔ULTRAVIOLET RADIATION

Inland Sea

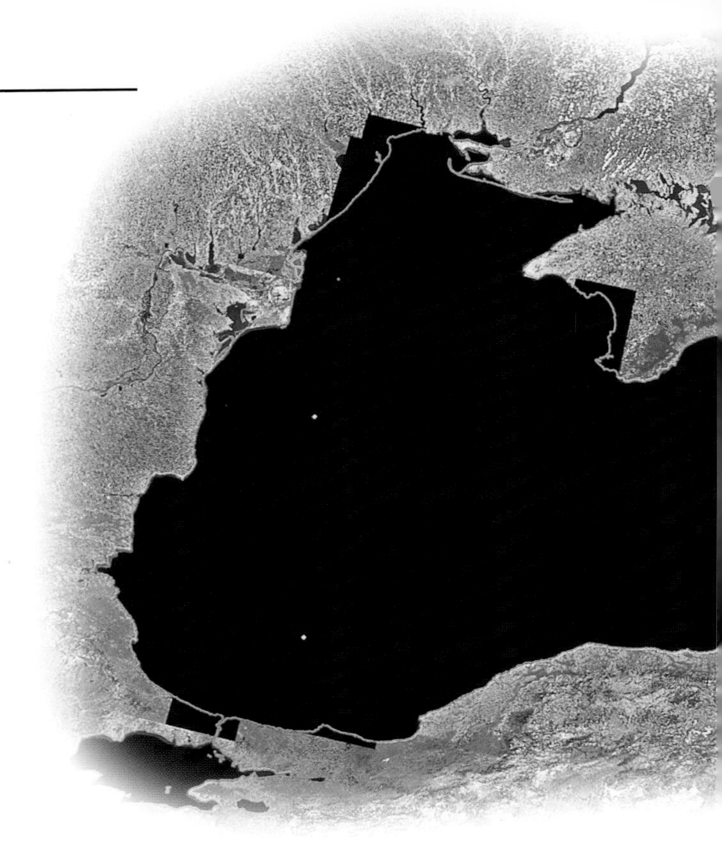

Large body of salty water, enclosed by land

A large body of salty water that is surrounded by land is called an inland sea. Inland seas are connected to another sea or ocean by a narrow strait (passage). Some very large lakes without a link to a sea are also generally classed as inland seas because of their size and because their waters are very salty. The world's largest inland sea is the Mediterranean Sea, with an area of 1,145,000 square miles (2,965,500 sq km). Other major inland seas include the Caspian, Aral, Black, and Dead Seas.

The Black Sea region. The small Sea of Azov is situated just above the center. At the bottom left is the Sea of Marmara, leading to the Mediterranean.

Caspian Sea

The Caspian Sea is the world's second largest inland sea, covering 152,239 square miles (394,300 sq km). Found in southwestern Russia and northern Iran, it has an average depth of 597 feet (179 m). The northern part of the sea is quite shallow, but the central and southern areas are deep. Salt levels in the water vary and are influenced by sea currents. The upper waters of the sea contain many species of marine creatures, but no life exists below a depth of 1,500 feet (450 m) because the water contains high concentrations of hydrogen sulfide.

The Caspian Sea currently lies 93 feet (28 m) below sea level, but its surface continues to get lower. Several rivers, including the Volga, flow into it, but the sea water evaporates quickly. Within the next 40 years, scientists estimate that its surface could drop as low as 100 feet (30 m) below sea level if plans to divert other rivers to empty into it are not carried out. The Caspian Sea is heavily used by ships, including large oil tankers, and is also used for commercial fishing.

HIGHLIGHTS

- Inland seas are large, enclosed bodies of water with a high salt content.
- The Mediterranean Sea is the largest inland sea, followed by the Caspian Sea.
- The Dead Sea contains water so salty that a person can easily float on its surface.

Aral Sea—the disappearing sea

The Aral Sea lies between Kazakhstan and Uzbekistan in central Asia. It is a good example of what can happen to an inland sea without careful management of its waters. In the early 1960s, the sea lay at about 170 feet (51 m) above sea level. It covered an area of 25,659 square miles (66,457 sq km) and had an average depth of 51 feet (15 m). Its waters contained fish similar to those found in the Caspian Sea to the west.

Only two rivers drain into the Aral. During the 1960s, the Soviet government decided to divert water from the rivers to irrigate (water) the surrounding land. The Aral Sea began to shrink quickly. By the 1980s, it had lost more than half its water. Rising salt levels killed most of its fish, and sea ports found themselves

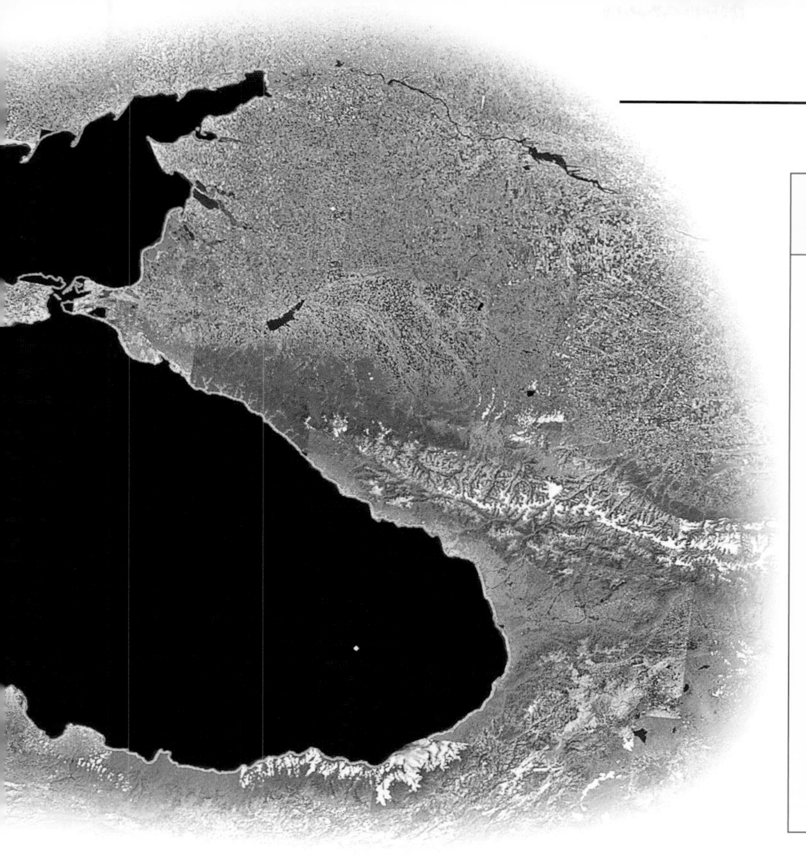

STORY OF SCIENCE

The Tethys Sea

In ancient times, other great inland seas existed on Earth. The Mediterranean, Caspian, Aral, and Dead Seas were all once part of a single, vast body of water called the Tethys Sea. This great ocean existed during the Mesozoic era, around 245 million to 65 million years ago. The existence of the Tethys Sea was first proposed in 1863 by Austrian geologist Eduard Suess (1831–1914). Suess based his theory on the evidence of sea rocks and fossils (FAH-suhlz; preserved evidence of past life) found high in the Alps in Europe and in the Himalayas. However, Suess's ideas were not generally accepted until the theory of plate tectonics, which supported them, became popular in the early 1970s.

stranded more than 30 miles (50 km) from the water. In 1992, the Aral Sea's surface area was only 13,000 square miles (33,800 sq km), with water three times saltier than 30 years before. In 1994, the states that relied on water from the two diverted rivers agreed to increase the flow into the Aral Sea. It is now beginning to grow again.

Black Sea

The Black Sea, found largely in southwestern Russia, has a surface area of 179,200 square miles (423,000 sq km). On average it is 4,000 feet (1,200 m) deep. In the southwest, the narrow Bosporus Strait links it to the Sea of Marmara, which in turn connects with the Mediterranean Sea. The Black Sea is fed by numerous freshwater rivers, including the Danube. Fresh water is less dense than salt water, so it generally remains at the surface, although strong currents at the Bosporus mix the salt and fresh water.

The waters of the Black Sea support life to a depth of 660 feet (200 m). Below that, high concentrations of hydrogen sulfide prohibit life except for some types of bacteria. The Black Sea is linked to the smaller Sea of Azov via the narrow Kerch Strait. This inland sea is 14,517 square miles (37,750 sq km) in size and is incredibly shallow, with a maximum depth of only 45 feet (13.5 m).

Dead Sea

The Dead Sea lies between Jordan and Israel in the Middle East and covers 538 square miles (1,393 sq km). A number of small streams flow into it, including the River Jordan, but the Dead Sea has no outlet. (Water is removed from the sea by evaporation.) Its northern end is deepest, but the southern parts are very shallow. The average depth is 460 feet (138 m).

The Dead Sea is famous for several reasons. First, at 1,302 feet (396 m) below sea level, it is the lowest body of water in the world. Second, it is notable for the very high salt content of its waters, which are up to seven times saltier than ocean water. The salt content increases with depth, but even at the surface, the water is so salty and dense that swimmers float easily and find it impossible to sink. The Dead Sea is frequently mentioned in the Bible.

The Dead Sea takes its name from the belief that its waters were too salty to support life. This is certainly true of fish and other sizeable marine animals, but tiny bacteria do live in the water, and a number of birds, mammals, and reptiles live along the shore.

CHECK THESE OUT!
✔LAKE ✔MEDITERRANEAN SEA
✔PLATE TECTONICS ✔RIVER

Ion

Single or bound groups of atoms that carry an electrical charge

There are three basic types of substances: simple molecular, macromolecular, and ionic. In a simple molecular substance, atoms of one or more elements are grouped together in molecules. Strong chemical bonds hold the atoms of the molecules together; weaker forces attract the molecules to one another. Simple molecular substances tend to be gases, liquids, or low-melting-point solids. In a macromolecular substance, all of the atoms are held together by strong chemical bonds. They are hard solids with high melting points, such as diamond, that do not dissolve in liquids. Ionic substances also tend to be hard solids with high melting points, but they do dissolve in some liquids, often water.

The properties of ionic solids come from their structures. They consist of positive and negative particles called ions, which form when atoms lose or gain electrons. The attractions between ions of opposite charges are very strong, which is what makes ionic solids hard that melt only at high temperatures.

EVERYDAY SCIENCE

Ion Exchange

A process called ion exchange can remove the ions that cause hardness in water. Water hardness shows as a crust on heating elements. One method of ion exchange uses synthetic minerals called zeolites (ZEE-oh-LYTS). These compounds of aluminum, oxygen, and silicon form structures that are full of tiny channels. Small amounts of sodium salts are added as the zeolite is made, and the sodium ions sit next to negatively charged sites within the channels. When hard water flows through these tiny channels, calcium and magnesium ions take up the positions of the sodium ions, which wash out with the softened water. After all the sodium has been washed away, the zeolite is returned to its original state by washing sodium chloride solution through it and removing the calcium and magnesium ions.

Ion formation

When a high voltage is applied to a neon sign it creates an electric field that is strong enough to separate a few electrons from the neon atoms. This leaves behind positively charged ions, called cations (CAT-EYE-uhnz). As the electrons and ions are pushed away from the electrodes of the same charge, they collide with additional atoms, forming more ions. Soon there are enough charged particles to conduct electricity throughout the sign. When the electrons and ions combine they emit light, so the sign glows. This is one way of forming ions.

In most cases, positive ions and negative ions form at the same time, when electrons transfer from atoms of one element to atoms of another. When sodium and chlorine react together, for example, sodium atoms lose one electron each to form sodium cations, Na^{+}. Chlorine atoms take on one electron each to become chloride ions, Cl^{-}. The general name for a negative ion is anion (AN-EYE-uhn). Just as neon atoms need the energy of a collision to lose an electron, sodium atoms require energy to lose an electron. Chlorine molecules (containing two chlorine

HIGHLIGHTS

- Ions are atoms, or groups of atoms, that carry positive or negative electrical charges.
- Passing a spark through a gas can form positive ions, called cations.
- Pairs of positive and negative ions form when electrons transfer from atoms of one element to atoms of another.

atoms) also require energy to split up into atoms and to take in electrons. The exact process, like most chemical reactions, proceeds by a number of steps and can be quite complicated. All matter involves atoms in motion, so the reaction will start with collisions between chlorine molecules and sodium atoms. The kinetic energy (energy of motion) of the particles bumping into each other will break the chlorine-chlorine bond and transfer an electron from the sodium atom to the chlorine atom. Since even one such reaction is stable, a little bit of heat energy is given off, and this powers more collisions. Eventually, small crystals of the solid are formed, which are far more stable than individual molecules (since in them, each ion is surrounded by six of the opposite charge) and additional heat is released.

Types of ions

Sodium and chloride ions are examples of the simplest type of ion. They are made from one atom each. Other ions contain two or more atoms. The atoms are held together by covalent

An ionic lattice, where anions and cations alternate with each other in an organized way.

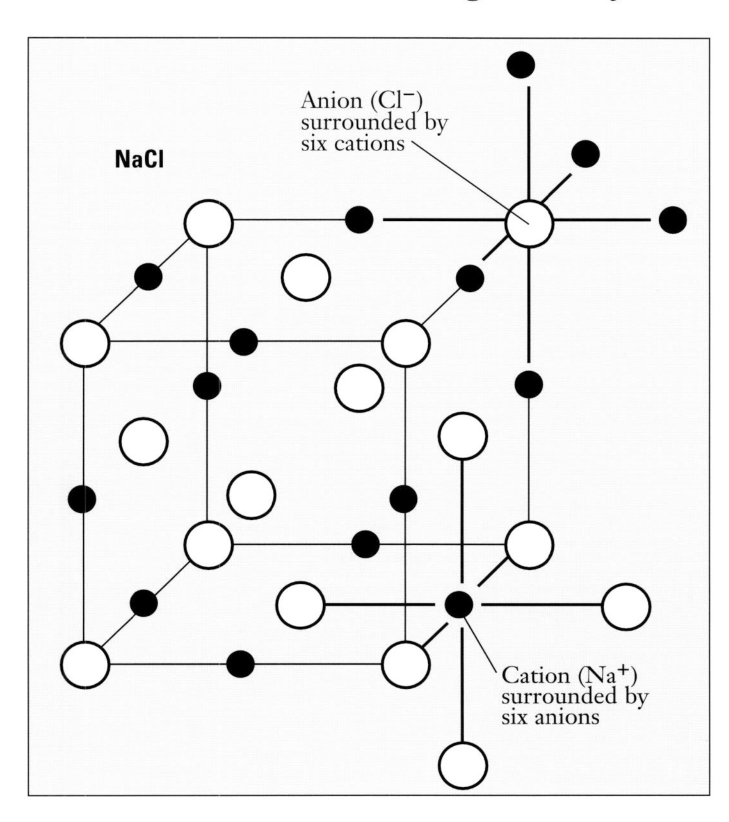

LOOK CLOSER

Free Radicals

Free radicals are atoms or groups of atoms that contain unpaired electrons. An example of free-radical formation happens when ultraviolet (UV) radiation shines on chlorine molecules. A chlorine molecule consists of two chlorine atoms joined by a pair of electrons in a covalent bond. If a chlorine molecule absorbs UV light, the energy can be enough to split the molecule into two parts. The electron pair splits up and leaves each chlorine atom with an unpaired electron. Unpaired electrons readily form bonds with other substances, so free radicals are usually extremely reactive.

When a free radical reacts with a stable molecule, its own unpaired electron becomes part of a bond by robbing another electron of its partner in a bond. This means that a new free radical forms. A chain of free radical reactions continues until two free radicals meet up and pair their electrons in a bond. Combustion (burning) and explosions are examples of free-radical chain reactions.

Sunlight and pollutants in the environment can cause free radicals to form. They are thought to hasten aging and possibly cause cancer. This is because they react with DNA and body tissues, causing changes to the genes and permanent tissue damage. Vitamins A, C, and E might reduce this damage by mopping up free radicals.

(shared-electron) bonds such as those found in molecules. The positive or negative charge is often spread through several atoms in the ion. Examples are ammonium ions, NH_4^+; nitrate ions, NO_3^-; and sulfate ions, SO_4^{2-}.

A third type of ion, a complex ion, consists of a positive metal ion surrounded by neutral molecules or anions that bond to it. These are called ligands (LIH-guhndz). Hexamine chromium (II) is a Cr^{2+} ion bonded to six neutral ammonia molecules (NH_3); hexacyanoferrate (III), is an Fe^{3+} ion bonded to six cyanide ions (CN^-), each with a single negative charge.

CHECK THESE OUT!
✔ACID AND BASE ✔ELECTROLYSIS ✔SALTS

Ionosphere

The upper layer of Earth's atmosphere that helps radio waves travel long distances

HIGHLIGHTS

- Radiation from the Sun turns a few atoms in the ionosphere into ions and free electrons.
- The ionosphere contains three main layers: the D, E, and F layers.
- Radio transmission is often better during the nighttime than during the day.

Why is it possible to hear radio stations from countries that are too far away to be seen? The answer to this mystery lies in a layer of the atmosphere called the ionosphere (eye-AH-nuh-SFIR), which can bend radio waves around Earth's curved surface. The bending effect allows radio waves to travel over much greater distances.

How the ionosphere works

The Sun sends out a stream of charged particles called the solar wind. Earth is surrounded by an atmosphere, a mixture of gases that are usually thought of as existing in a number of separate layers. In the upper layers of the atmosphere, the solar wind turns a small fraction (barely 0.4 percent) of the atoms into electrically charged particles called ions and free (unattached) electrons. The region where these ions exist is called the ionosphere.

The charged ions in the ionosphere can reflect radio waves back to Earth in much the same way that a piece of glass reflects light waves. If a flashlight is shone at right angles at a piece of glass, the beam shoots straight through and little if any light is reflected back. When the flashlight is aimed at a certain shallow angle, called the critical angle, an ordinary piece of glass will reflect the light just like a mirror, with no light passing through. This is exactly what happens in the ionosphere. The angle depends on the frequency (rate of waves passing a fixed point each second) of the light (or radio waves) used, and the ever-changing nature of the ionosphere must also be taken into account.

The ionosphere is in a state of constant change because it owes its existence to sunlight. The way in which sunlight reaches different parts of Earth is constantly changing. The ionosphere changes between daytime and nighttime, with the seasons of the year, with solar eclipses, and with

Earth's atmosphere is shown here as seen at sunset from orbit. Vast clouds are silhouetted against the Sun.

other changes in the Sun's radiation. These changes in the ionosphere mean radio waves are transmitted in different ways at different times.

Layers of the ionosphere

Scientists have managed to identify three distinct layers of the ionosphere with particular properties, called the D, E, and F layers. Closest to Earth, the D layer extends from around 30 to 55 miles (50 to 90 km). It consists of negative ions that have been produced from nitric oxide by ultraviolet light and X rays in the solar wind. The E layer extends from roughly 55 to 90 miles (90 to 140 km). Here, ions are produced from oxygen molecules both by the solar wind and by meteors (solid objects created from asteroids or comets). The F layer extends from 90 to 300 miles (140 to 480 km). This layer is made of two sublayers, the F_1 layer from 90 to 125 miles (140 to 200 km) and the F_2 layer from 125 to 300 miles (200 to 480 km).

The ionosphere is constantly changing. The D layer is produced mostly by solar radiation and so disappears when sunlight disappears. For the same reason, the E layer weakens and the F_1 and F_2 layers merge. During the daytime, the lower layers of the ionosphere absorb and weaken radio waves. As these layers disappear at night, radio waves can be transmitted over much greater distances. This explains why it is possible to hear many more distant radio stations at night than during the daytime.

The age of radio

Radio became an important new method of transmitting information in 1899 when Irish-Italian scientist Guglielmo Marconi (1874–1937) showed that radio waves could travel over 60 miles (100 km). Although scientists had long suspected part of the atmosphere could conduct electricity, it was not until Marconi's successful experiment that they began to realize how that process might work.

In 1902, U.S. engineer Arthur Kennelly (1861–1939) realized that the ionosphere must exist, and British physicist Oliver Heaviside (1850–1925) worked out the theory of how it might operate. Their discovery, the E layer, was named the Kennelly–Heaviside layer. It was confirmed by British physicist Edward Appleton (1892–1955), who later found the F layer (sometimes called the Appleton layer in his honor). Once scientists properly understood how the ionosphere worked, they were able to design much more efficient radio transmitters and receivers, and the age of radio was born.

LOOK CLOSER

Nighttime Radio

During the daytime, waves from an AM (amplitude modulation) radio transmitter shoot up into the atmosphere. While the sunlight is strong, the D and E layers of the ionosphere are also quite strong. They tend to trap the radio waves and prevent them from reaching the higher F layer of the ionosphere that can bounce them back to Earth. As a result, relatively few waves are reflected back during the daytime, and daytime radio stations are not broadcast very far.

At nighttime, sunlight disappears and the D and E layers of the ionosphere are much weaker. Many more waves can therefore get through to the F layer, which bounces them around Earth's curved surface. Consequently, radio waves can travel much farther. This explains why many more AM stations can be heard at night, and from much farther afield. It also explains nighttime interference—many more radio waves are able to interact with each other and therefore affect the quality of the sound.

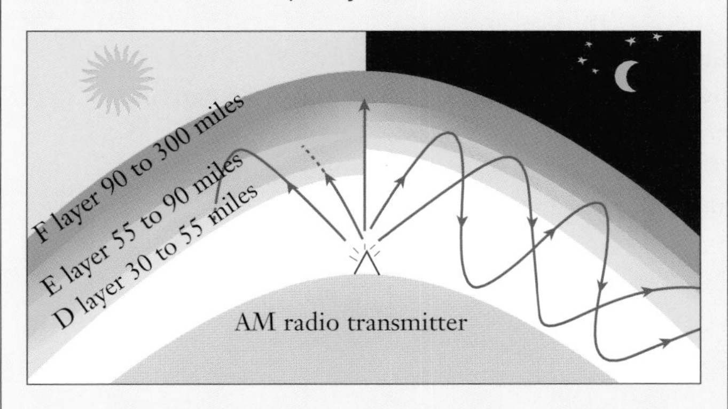

At night, AM radio waves reach the higher regions of the atmosphere and are transmitted for hundreds of miles.

CHECK THESE OUT!
✔ATMOSPHERE ✔ELECTRON ✔ION ✔RADIO WAVE ✔STRATOSPHERE ✔SUN

Iron and Steel

Two forms of a metal that is the most important building material in the world

One of the most important developments in the history of humankind was ancient people's discovery of iron and their gradual understanding of how to work it. Iron ores make up 5 percent of Earth's crust. Earth's core is mostly molten iron and nickel. Iron also arrives on Earth as fragments of meteorites (small particles of matter in space). Iron was very important to the ancient Romans. Its chemical symbol, Fe, comes from the Latin word *ferrum*.

Pure iron is a gray, shiny metal with a melting point of 2800°F (1536°C). When completely pure, iron is not particularly hard. In the state in which it is extracted from its ores, however, it usually contains small quantities of carbon. Carbon makes the iron harder and stronger, and also lowers its melting point. This fact is important for iron's use in manufacture.

This man must wear protective clothing while taking a sample from a blast furnace.

HIGHLIGHTS

- Iron is an important construction material. It is used to make both ships and cars.
- Small amounts of metals such as cobalt can be added to steel to make stronger steel alloys.

As an element, iron forms a group with the metals cobalt and nickel. All three are affected by magnets, but iron is more strongly affected than any other element. Once magnetized, it retains its magnetism, becoming a magnet itself. This process is called ferromagnetism. Cobalt and nickel are the only other ferromagnetic elements at normal temperatures. They are ferromagnetic because their atoms line up to form strong magnetic regions called domains. If a long iron bar is lined up with Earth's magnetic field and hit with a hammer, this force is enough to make the iron atoms line up. Stroking a rod of iron with a magnet will have the same effect. A magnet should never be struck repeatedly or it may lose

its magnetism. Magnetized iron will also lose its magnetism if it is heated above 1410°F (766°C).

In compounds with other elements, iron can be in either a +2 (ferrous) state or a +3 (ferric) state. The main ores of iron are hematite (ferric oxide, Fe_2O_3) and magnetite (Fe_3O_4). Nearly all ores and minerals contain traces of iron.

Manufacture of iron and steel

The earliest way of making iron from its oxides softened the metal but did not melt it. A pile of ore and charcoal was set on fire. The charcoal reacted with oxygen in the ore, releasing iron and carrying off carbon monoxide. A sponge of fairly pure iron called a bloom was left. This was hammered while white-hot, driving out gas and impurities. As it could be worked into shape, the iron was called wrought (RAWT; worked) iron.

This way of producing iron continued into the 19th century. Meanwhile, a type of furnace was invented that used air pumped from a bellows to make the fire hot enough to melt the iron. This was an early form of today's blast furnace. The molten iron metal was cast in molds dug in sand. It was called cast iron and formed a central bar with other bars attached along both sides.

Cast iron is much harder than wrought iron. It contains more carbon, so it cannot be hammered. In 1784, Englishman Henry Cort (1740–1800) patented his puddling furnace to burn away most of this carbon. Fuel was burned at the back of the furnace, and the flames passed under a low roof to melt pig iron (a crude form of iron) at the front so the iron did not come into contact with the fuel. The iron from this furnace contained very little carbon and was used to make steel.

Steel contains only 0.05 to 1.6 percent carbon. Around 1856, Englishman Henry Bessemer (1813–1898) developed a process to change molten pig iron into steel by blowing air through it. Since 1953, oxygen has been used instead of air in the basic oxygen process. This process produces carbon steel (the simplest and cheapest to produce). Carbon steel is used for automobile bodies, machinery, and ship construction.

Iron has one great failing: it rusts. Rust is ferric oxide (Fe_2O_3) and is caused by contact with oxygen in damp conditions. Contact with oxygen and water in the air can be prevented by coating the iron with paint, one of the most widely used protective coatings. Steel cans can be coated with tin, and zinc can also be deposited on iron to make galvanized iron.

Adding small amounts of other metals to steel produces alloy steels for special purposes. Stainless steel, which does not rust, contains more than 10 percent chromium. Nickel makes steel resistant to pulling stresses. Other metals that can be added to steel to make it harder or stronger include cobalt, aluminum, titanium, and molybdenum (muh-LIB-duh-nuhm).

EVERYDAY SCIENCE

The Blast Furnace

Iron is extracted from its ores in a blast furnace made from steel lined with firebrick to withstand the high temperatures developed. A mixture of iron ore, coke, and limestone (called the charge) is fed into the top of the furnace, and hot air is blown into the bottom through vents called tuyeres (twee-YERZ). The carbon of the coke reacts with the iron oxide to form carbon dioxide gas, while molten iron trickles down to the base of the furnace. Impurities in the ore react with the limestone to form slag. Slag is also molten and flows down to float on top of the iron. Molten iron is drawn off at the bottom of the furnace and the slag is drawn off above it. As this happens, more charge is fed into the top so that the process can continue.

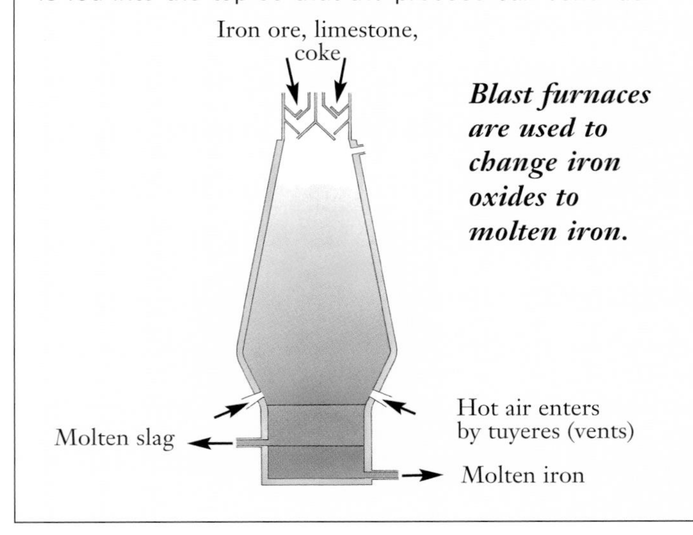

Blast furnaces are used to change iron oxides to molten iron.

CHECK THESE OUT!

✔ALLOY ✔MAGNETISM ✔METAL ✔SMELTING

Island

Relatively small mass of dry land surrounded by water

Relatively small areas of land entirely surrounded by water are called islands. The geography and landscape of an island depend on factors such as its location, origin, age, and the degree to which it is isolated from the mainland. The climate of islands varies less than that of continents because they are surrounded by ocean.

Over long periods of time, islands rise from the sea and may also disappear again beneath the water. Their emergence and disappearance depends on the region's geography, and often on the geological upheaval taking place deep inside Earth's crust. Many former islands are now completely submerged under the sea. If sea levels were to rise significantly in the future, many low-lying islands that exist today would disappear beneath the waves.

A Pacific atoll situated among the Caroline Islands. Atolls are coral islands surrounded by lagoons.

Types of islands

Geographers divide islands into two groups: continental and oceanic islands. Continental islands lie close to continents, often on the continental shelf (the shallow sea bed that surrounds them). The water around continental islands is therefore usually no more than 590 feet (180 m) deep. Most continental islands were once attached to the mainland. The British Isles and Sri Lanka, which is situated off the southern tip of India, are both good examples of large continental islands.

Oceanic islands, called seamounts, are very different. They lie a long way from the nearest continent and rise up from the floors of deep oceans. They are made mainly of the volcanic rock basalt.

HIGHLIGHTS

- Islands are relatively small areas of dry land surrounded by water.
- Islands are divided by geographers into two groups: continental and oceanic islands.
- Islands are usually made up of volcanic rock basalt or limestone, or both.
- Islands may be made of a variety of rocks. Some oceanic islands are made of basalt or limestone.

How islands form

Both the dry land and the oceans rest on Earth's crust. However, this crust is not of the same thickness everywhere. Under oceans, it is quite thin, around 6 miles (9 km) thick. Under continents, it is around 34 miles (55 km) thick.

Earth's crust and part of the upper mantle are not one continuous layer. It is made of a number of huge tectonic plates, which fit together like pieces in a jigsaw puzzle. These plates are not still, but drift very slowly over Earth's mantle. Over vast periods of time, plates drift apart, collide, or rub against one another. Earthquakes and volcanoes are common along the boundaries where the plates meet. The formation of many islands is connected with such volcanic eruptions.

Many oceanic islands are made of coral-based limestone or basalt, a rock erupted from volcanoes. Most began life as volcanoes on the ocean floor. In time, the rock erupted by the undersea volcano built up so much that it reached the surface of the sea to form an island. Most volcanic islands form at the boundaries where two tectonic plates meet and Earth's crust is thinnest. This allows molten rock from inside Earth to well up on the surface.

Some islands form where tectonic plates collide or push against each other. Other islands form where plates pull apart. Lava (LAH-vuh; molten rock) wells up through the crust, often forming a long ridge, which is a chain of undersea mountains, such as the Mid-Atlantic Ridge in the Atlantic Ocean. The large island of Iceland is part of the ridge. It straddles the boundary between two tectonic plates.

Not all volcanic islands form around plate boundaries. Some undersea volcanoes erupt in the middle of plates in areas called hot spots. As the plate moves very slowly over the hot spot, so a chain of islands may form.

Atolls and barrier islands

In warm, shallow waters, corals grow around isolated seamounts to form fringing reefs. If the island later subsides (sinks), a ring-shaped reef called an atoll will be all that remains.

Barrier islands are sandy islands that lie off mainland coasts, parallel to the shore. Most barrier islands formed around 5,000 to 6,000 years ago, after the end of the last ice age. As sea levels rose to flood the continental shelves, waves caused erosion that created sandy deposits. Large piles of sand built up to form long bars that eventually broke the sea surface to form islands.

Many islands are the result of changes in sea level. For example, the British Isles and their offshore islands and the many small islands off the Scandinavian coast were created following the sea-level changes that caused widespread flooding after the ice age.

LOOK CLOSER

Large and Small

Greenland is the world's largest island. It is not made of volcanic rock or limestone but of Precambrian crystalline metamorphic gneiss. It is closely related to the Canadian Shield region. It has an area of 840,000 square miles (2.2 million sq km). New Zealand, which has some volcanic rock and much sediment, covers 103,384 square miles (270,000 sq km). Suwarrow, in the Cook Islands, is one of the world's smallest islands, with an area of only around 2 square miles (5 sq km).

Island life

The range of living organisms on islands is often different from that on the nearest mainland. This is because only certain types of living organisms have been able to reach and colonize the island. Plants whose seeds are carried by wind or water are able to cross the watery barrier to root on islands. Flying animals such as birds, bats, and insects may have arrived under their own power or carried by strong air currents. Other creatures may have arrived on rafts of floating vegetation.

Once on the island, species (types) of organisms often evolve (slowly develop) in ways different from populations on the mainland. This is because of the difference in environments. On an island, there may be fewer predators to threaten weaker animals, or fewer animals generally, and so less competition for food. There are disadvantages to living on an island. Whole species may be wiped out by events such as violent storms or volcanic eruptions because there is no chance to leave the island and then return.

CHECK THESE OUT!
✔CONTINENTAL SHELF ✔EROSION
✔OCEAN ✔PLATE TECTONICS ✔VOLCANO

Isomer

A structural arrangement of elements differing from another with the same molecular formula

Molecules are collections of atoms that are linked together by chemical bonds. Just as a set of building blocks can be put together in different ways, a set of atoms can assemble themselves into different molecules. Both the chemical and physical properties of these different molecules, named isomers (EYE-suh-muhrz), can differ widely.

Structural isomers

Structural isomerism happens when atoms are linked together in different arrangements. The formula C_2H_6O can represent two different compounds. In dimethyl ether (EE-thur; CH_3OCH_3), two methyl groups (CH_3) are linked to an oxygen atom. It is a gas that liquefies at –76°F (–24°C). Ethanol (ETH-uh-NOL; C_2H_5OH) is a liquid that boils at 172°F (78°C). The difference between the boiling points of these compounds is so great because ethanol's hydroxy (-OH) group forms attractions called hydrogen bonds between molecules (a hydrogen atom is attracted to a lone pair of electrons on an oxygen atom). Dimethyl ether cannot form these bonds so it boils more easily.

The alkanes (AL-KAYNZ) are hydrocarbons with the general formula C_nH_{2n+2}, where n can be any number. There are alternative structures for any alkane with four or more carbon atoms. Butane (BYOO-TAYN; C_4H_{10}) and methylpropane (METH-yl-PROH-PAYN; $CH_3CH(CH_3)CH_3$) are the two structural isomers of C_4 alkanes. There are three isomers with the formula C_5H_{12}: pentane (C_5H_{12}), 2,2-dimethylpropane ($CH_3C(CH_3)_2CH_3$), and 2-methylbutane ($CH_3CH(CH_3)CH_2CH_3$). The number of possible isomers increases rapidly with the number of carbon atoms. For example, there are 75 isomers of $C_{10}H_{22}$.

Positional isomerism is a form of structural isomerism in which two or more molecules have the same functional groups (groups of atoms responsible for the characteristic reactions of a compound) attached in different ways. The compounds 1-bromo-1-nitroethane and 1-bromo-2-nitroethane are positional isomers. One isomer has both functional groups—bromo and nitro—attached to the same carbon atom. The other has the two groups attached to different carbon atoms. The properties of positional isomers can differ greatly.

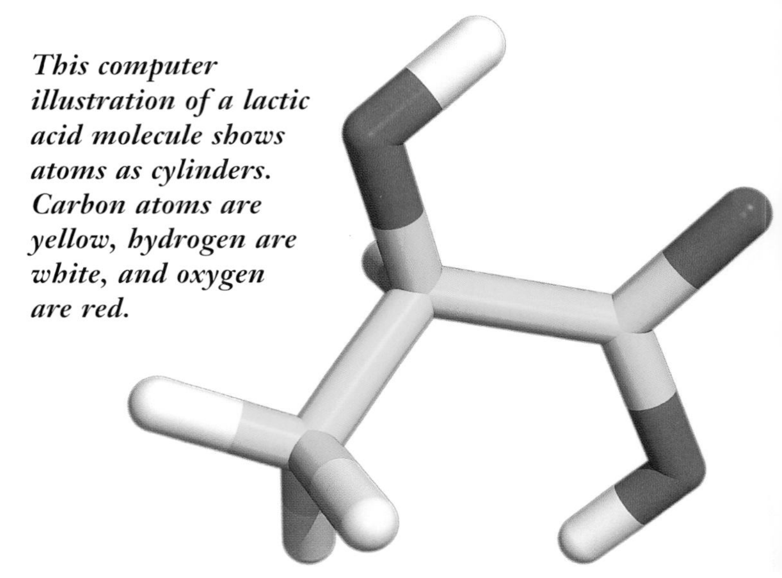

This computer illustration of a lactic acid molecule shows atoms as cylinders. Carbon atoms are yellow, hydrogen are white, and oxygen are red.

Aromatic positional isomers

Positional isomerism can happen with compounds based on benzene (BEN-zeen), a six-carbon ring. Each carbon atom has a hydrogen atom attached to it. When benzene reacts with other substances, these hydrogen atoms are often replaced by other groups of atoms, called substituents. The properties of molecules with more than one substituent on the

HIGHLIGHTS

- Isomers are compounds that are structurally different but have identical numbers of atoms of each element.
- Isomers often have different chemical and physical properties.

LOOK CLOSER

Chiral Compounds

Natural substances such as proteins and sugars are optically active—they rotate the plane of polarized light (light that is all traveling in the same plane) clockwise or counterclockwise as it passes through them. This is because they are chiral. Normally, living organisms produce only the isomer that rotates light counterclockwise. This isomer is called the L enantiomer. Molecules that rotate light clockwise are known as the D enantiomer.

Many pharmaceuticals (drugs) are chiral. Often, one enantiomer has more of a beneficial effect than the other. Sometimes, the ineffective enantiomer can cause harmful side effects. Many chemists and pharmaceutical companies are researching ways of manufacturing single-enantiomer drugs, rather than the equal mixtures of both isomers that are made by standard chemical processes.

benzene ring depend on the substituents' relative positions. When benzene reacts with nitric acid, the product contains three compounds with the formula of dinitrobenzene: $C_6H_4(NO_2)_2$. The three isomers are named by numbering one of the substituted carbon atoms "1" and counting around the ring. The isomer with nitro

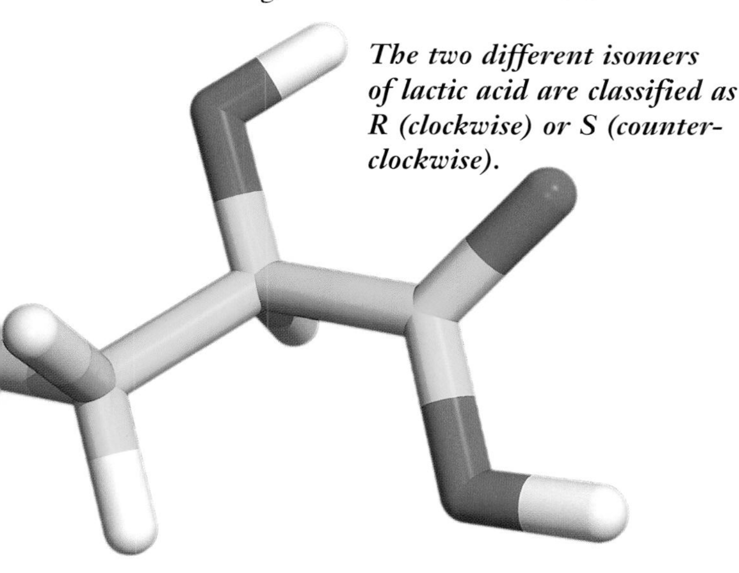

The two different isomers of lactic acid are classified as R (clockwise) or S (counter-clockwise).

groups on adjacent carbons in the ring is called 1,2-dinitrobenzene (dy-NY-troh-BEN-zeen). The isomer with the second nitro group on the next carbon along is 1,3-dinitrobenzene. The isomer with nitro groups on opposite sides of the ring is 1,4-dinitrobenzene.

Cis-trans isomers

Parts of a molecule joined by a single bond are usually free to rotate (spin) around the bond unless it is part of a ring. Rotation is not possible around a double bond and this gives rise to a type of isomerism called stereoisomerism. An example is 1,2-dibromoethene, (CHBr=CHBr). The atoms in 1,2-dibromoethene all lie in a flat plane. One form of 1,2-dibromoethene has both bromine (BROH-MEEN) atoms situated on the same side of the double bond. This isomer is called cis-1,2-dibromoethene. Trans-1,2-dibromoethene has a bromine atom on each side.

Chiral centers

If a structural formula includes a carbon atom bonded to four different atoms it is called a chiral (KY-ruhl) center. Chiral centers can have two mirror-image isomers arranged around them. This is because atoms arrange themselves in a tetrahedron around a singly bonded carbon atom. A tetrahedron is similar to a pyramid, but it has a three-sided base. Lactic acid can be made in two mirror-image forms called enantiomers. The carbon atom that causes this property, known as chirality, is at the molecule's center. It has attached to it one hydrogen atom (H), one hydroxy group (-OH), one methyl group ($-CH_3$), and one carboxylic acid group ($-CO_2H$).

Enantiomers of the same formula are identical in every respect except two. First, they rotate the polarized light (light waves that are all traveling in the same plane) by the same amount but in opposite directions. Second, they often react with other chiral molecules in different ways, if the chiral center is involved in the reaction.

CHECK THESE OUT!

✔CARBOHYDRATE ✔CARBON ✔HYDROCARBON

Isotope

An atom with a different number of neutrons in its nucleus than other atoms of the same element

Atoms (the building blocks of chemical elements) of the same element that have different numbers of neutrons are called isotopes (EYE-suh-TOHPS). The chemical properties of an atom depend on how many electrons the atom has and how strongly its nucleus attracts those electrons. These factors depend only on the number of protons in the nucleus. It is this number, called the atomic number, that defines each element. The isotopes of an element all have the same chemical properties.

Atomic mass and isotopes

Each isotope is described by an atomic mass number, a whole number equal to the number of protons and neutrons in the nucleus. The most common isotope of carbon has six protons and six neutrons. Its atomic number is 6, its mass number is 12, and the isotope is called carbon 12. Carbon 13 has seven neutrons. Carbon 14 has eight. Scientists define an atomic mass unit as one-twelfth of the mass of an atom of carbon 12, that is, the mass of the nucleus containing six protons and six neutrons together with the mass of six electrons. Masses of neutrons and protons are almost identical. Each is about one atomic mass unit. The mass of the electron is one-two thousandth of this, so can usually be neglected.

HIGHLIGHTS

- Isotopes of an element have identical chemical properties but different atomic masses.
- Techniques for separating isotopes depend on their slight differences in mass.
- There are 287 naturally occuring stable isotopes.

This radiographer is preparing a patient for radiotherapy. Isotopes are used in radiotherapy to stop the growth of tumors and destroy them.

The mass of an atom of an isotope in atomic mass units will be nearly equal to its atomic mass number. It is not equal because protons and neutrons differ slightly in mass, and a small amount of mass is converted into energy and released when the nucleus is formed. Since almost all naturally occuring elements have more than one stable isotope—the only exceptions being aluminum, beryllium (buh-RIL-ee-uhm), phosphorus (FAHS-fuh-ruhs), and sodium—chemists use a set of average atomic masses. The average atomic mass of carbon is 12.01, since an average sample will contain small amounts of heavier carbon 13 and carbon 14. Chlorine (KLOR-EEN) is a mixture of 76 percent chlorine 35 with 24 percent chlorine 37, so its relative atomic mass is 35.46.

Separation

Techniques for separating isotopes depend on their different atomic weights. One such technique is used to enrich uranium for use as nuclear fuel and in weapons. Uranium hexafluoride is a gas. If pumped through a series of microscopic filters, uranium 235 hexafluoride passes through slightly faster than heavier

STORY OF SCIENCE

Willard Libby and Carbon Dating

In 1947, U.S. chemist Willard Libby (1908–1980) developed carbon dating as a way of estimating the age of animal and plant remains. Plants take in carbon dioxide from the air to form carbohydrates and other tissues. When they die, carbon 14 in their remains gradually decays to nitrogen 14. Libby heated samples of plant-based materials to convert them into soot, which is a form of carbon. He then weighed the soot and placed it in a radiation detector to measure the amount of carbon 14 in the sample. He calculated the ages of samples from the ratio of carbon isotopes. Textiles such as cotton, which are made from plants, can be dated in this way, as can the remains of animals that fed on plants.

Libby assumed the ratio of carbon isotopes in the air to be constant. This is because carbon 14 is created in the atmosphere by radiation from the Sun converting nitrogen 14 atoms into carbon 14 atoms. When around one in a billion carbon atoms are carbon 14, the rate of carbon 14 decay matches the rate of carbon 14 formation, so the overall quantity stays the same. In the 1970s, studies of annual pollen layers trapped in the Greenland icecap showed that the intensity of the Sun has varied by up to 10 percent in the last 10,000 years, so adjustments have to be made. Future archeologists will also have to make adjustments when they study samples from the last two centuries. The burning of fossil fuels released huge quantities of old carbon dioxide into the air, reducing the ratio of carbon 14. Atomic-weapons tests in the late 20th century also distorted the natural ratio by creating additional carbon 14.

uranium 238 hexafluoride. After thousands of these diffusion processes, up to 90 percent pure uranium 235 hexafluoride is produced.

Stability and radioactivity

Most nuclei contain a number of neutrons between one and one-and-a-half times the number of protons. Only certain combinations of neutrons and protons are stable; other combinations change by radioactive decay. Altogether, there are 287 natural, stable isotopes. Isotopes that spontaneously decay are called radioisotopes. Some are natural; others are made by nuclear reactions. There are no stable isotopes with atomic numbers greater than 83. There are two main types of radioactive decay: alpha and beta. In alpha decay, an unstable nucleus ejects an alpha particle, which is a group of two protons and two neutrons. The result is a nucleus whose atomic number is two units less than the starting nucleus, and whose mass number is four units less. In beta decay, a nucleus ejects an electron and a neutron becomes a proton. Beta decay causes the atomic number to increase by one unit while the mass number stays the same. In a third type of decay, the antiparticle of an electron, called a positron, is ejected and a proton becomes a neutron. The mass number remains the same, but the atomic number decreases by one unit. The same can happen if a nucleus captures an electron from an inner electron shell or a nearby beta-emitting isotope.

Isotopes in medicine

Isotopes of certain elements are used to diagnose and treat diseases. For example, cobalt 60 produces beta particles and gamma rays as it converts to nickel 60, which is stable. This radiation is used to kill cancer cells. Positron-emitting isotopes can be injected into the bloodstream of patients with suspected brain conditions. When the isotope decays, its positrons combine with electrons to form gamma rays. The gamma rays are detected and used to produce images of blood vessels in the brain.

CHECK THESE OUT!

✔ELEMENT ✔RADIOACTIVITY ✔RADIOCARBON DATING

Jet Stream

Fast-moving current of air that flows high above the surface of Earth

Fast-moving currents of air that flow high in the atmosphere, about 6 to 9 miles (10 to 14 km) above the surface of Earth, are called jet streams. The strength and location of these air currents change on a daily basis and with the seasons.

Scientists divide Earth's atmosphere into five layers starting from Earth's surface: the troposphere, the stratosphere, the mesosphere, the thermosphere, and the exosphere. The troposphere is the lowest layer, extending about 6 miles (10 km) from the planet's surface. Beyond that is the stratosphere, 6 to 30 miles (10 to 50 km) high.

In the upper troposphere and the stratosphere, winds regularly blow from west to east, except near the equator (an imaginary circle around Earth at equal distances from the North and South Poles). These winds are called the upper-air westerlies. Jet streams are at the core of these high-level westerly winds.

Jet streams were discovered during World War II (1939–1945), when military aircraft first flew high enough to encounter them. In the world of flying, winds that blow in the same direction as an aircraft is traveling are called tailwinds. Winds that blow in the opposite direction are called headwinds. As tailwinds, jet streams increase the speed and fuel efficiency of aircraft. As headwinds, they have the opposite effect. World War II bombers slowed down when flying directly into jet streams.

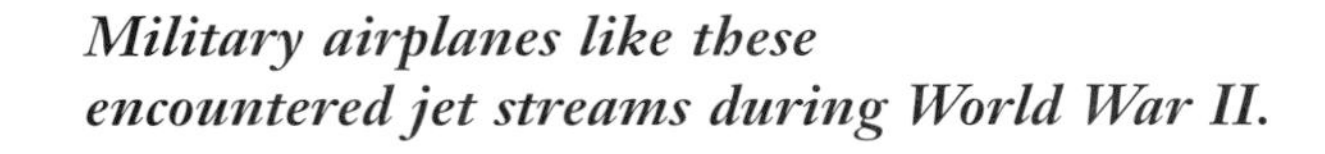

Military airplanes like these encountered jet streams during World War II.

HIGHLIGHTS

- Jet streams are fast-flowing currents of air high in Earth's atmosphere. These high-level winds flow mainly from west to east.
- Jet streams vary daily and with the seasons. In turn, they affect weather conditions on a local and global scale.
- Jet streams affect the speed and fuel efficiency of airliners. They were discovered by high-flying military aircraft during World War II.

Even today, these strong winds affect the flying times of modern aircraft. A powerful tailwind can shave an hour off the journey time of an airliner flying from New York to London. Jet streams also threaten the safety of aircraft by causing strong turbulence (swirling currents).

Jet streams vary with the seasons. They affect weather conditions by influencing the location and strength of weather fronts and areas of high and low pressure.

What causes jet streams?

The high winds of jet streams are caused by differences in air temperature and pressure between polar and tropical regions. The most powerful jet streams occur in winter. At the center of the jet stream, winds sometimes reach speeds of over 250 miles per hour (400 km/h).

These strong winds are found inside a narrow band about 50 miles (80 km) wide. Jet stream winds can flow for thousands of miles, circling Earth with a serpentine, or wavy, course. Since they move air around Earth, jet streams are also important in transferring heat around the planet.

Major jet streams

Each of Earth's hemispheres has two major jet streams. The most important streams, for both air travel and weather forecasting, are the polar-front jet streams. In both hemispheres, these jets flow from west to east in a wavy path. In the Northern Hemisphere, the polar-front jet stream generally lies between 30 and 60 degrees north, in a region where the low-level prevailing winds, the polar northeasterlies, meet the middle-altitude westerlies.

The path of the polar-front jet stream varies greatly from day to day. Meteorologists (scientists who study the weather) carefully watch the movements of this jet and use mathematical models of the atmosphere to predict its behavior in advance.

The second major jet stream is the subtropical jet, which flows closer to the equator, at between 2 and 50 degrees latitude in each hemisphere. In the Northern Hemisphere, the subtropical jet flows roughly from southwest to northeast, and occurs where prevailing winds, called trade winds, meet the westerlies of the mid-latitudes.

A jet stream is a current of air that travels in a wavy west-to-east direction. The jet stream forms a boundary between the colder air to the north and the warmer air to the south.

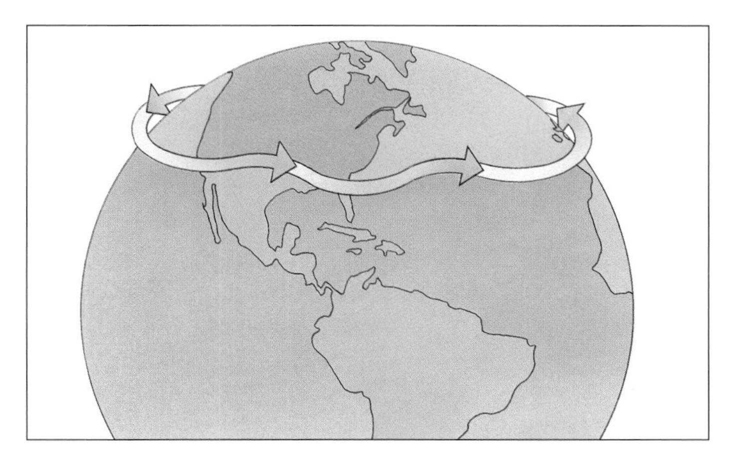

LOOK CLOSER

Weather Maps

Weather maps represent jet streams as wavy ribbons of air. These strong air currents flow from west to east except near the equator. In the Northern Hemisphere, jet streams form a boundary between the colder air toward the north and the warmer air toward the south.

Jet streams change their position constantly, moving up and down in the atmosphere as well as to the north or south. Weather experts have to pay close attention to the movement of jet streams because daily changes in their positions, no matter how small, can affect local weather conditions. Larger, long-lasting movements of jet streams can lead to droughts (excessively dry periods), heat waves, cold snaps, and floods when they divert weather systems from their normal routes.

Jet streams change with the seasons, mainly in response to variations in air temperatures between the north and the south during summer and winter. During the summer months, jet streams usually grow weaker and move farther north. The subtropical jet almost disappears, except for a portion, situated over the Mediterranean Sea, that blows from west to east at lower speeds.

There are several other minor jet streams that flow at certain times of the year. The equatorial jet stream flows from east to west over Southeast Asia and Africa during the summer. Scientists believe that it is related to the warming of air over high mountain ranges. This jet steam influences the arrival of the summer monsoons in India and Africa, and also determines how long these heavy rains last. The monsoons are vital for farming in these regions. Another jet stream, the polar night jet, flows high in the atmosphere, over 9 miles (14 km) above Earth's surface. This air current moves generally eastward but only blows in winter.

CHECK THESE OUT!

✔AIR PRESSURE ✔ATMOSPHERE
✔MONSOON ✔WEATHER ✔WIND

Jupiter

The largest planet in the Solar System

The fifth planet from the Sun, Jupiter is the largest world in the Solar System. It is a very different planet from Earth because it is made almost entirely of gas. Jupiter has a huge atmosphere wrapped around a quite small solid core. Jupiter also has thin rings and a huge family of moons in orbit around it, including four that are complex worlds in themselves.

A gas giant

Jupiter is the closest to Earth of the Solar System's four gas giants. (The other three are Saturn, Uranus, and Neptune.) Jupiter lies beyond the asteroid belt of small, starlike bodies that separates it from the much smaller rocky terrestrial planets, including Earth. Jupiter is vast, with a diameter of 88,700 miles (142,700 km). Although it is made up of light gases, mostly hydrogen, helium, and ammonia, Jupiter is also by far the heaviest planet in the Solar System. It weighs more than twice as much as the rest of the planets combined.

Jupiter is the second brightest planet as seen from Earth (only Venus appears brighter), and it takes nearly 12 years to orbit the Sun. To the naked eye, it appears as a brilliant yellowish-white star. Binoculars or a small telescope show it as a disk with faint bands across it, usually accompanied by four faint starlike bodies. These bodies are Jupiter's four main moons: Io, Europa, Ganymede, and Callisto.

Jupiter's huge mass gives it huge gravity, which creates high pressures and heats the inside of the planet. Jupiter is unusual because it radiates more energy into space than it receives from the Sun. Some scientists have called it a failed star. If Jupiter was larger, its gravity might have made the center of the planet hot enough to begin nuclear reactions and shine like the Sun.

This collage shows Jupiter and its four planet-size moons called the Galilean satellites. They are not shown to scale but are in their relative positions.

HIGHLIGHTS

- Jupiter is one of four giant gas planets in the Solar System.
- There are at least 16 moons circling Jupiter. The four main moons are Io, Europa, Ganymede, and Callisto.
- One of Jupiter's features is the Great Red Spot, which is thought to be a gigantic storm.

No one knows whether there is a solid core deep inside Jupiter's atmosphere or whether the planet is just a huge ball of gas. Astronomers think much of the planet's atmosphere is unchanged from when it first formed along with the rest of the Solar System, some 4.6 billion years ago.

Jupiter's atmosphere

Space probes such as *Voyager 1* and *Voyager 2* have shown that Jupiter's atmosphere is a swirling mixture of gases, forming whirlpools and high-speed streams around the planet. Wind speeds at Jupiter's surface are around 330 mph (540 km/h). The high winds are driven by Jupiter's rapid rotation. The planet rotates so fast—once in 10 hours—that it is not spherical. Instead it bulges out at the equator.

Although Jupiter's weather seems just as unpredictable and chaotic as Earth's, the atmosphere does break down into just a few permanent weather systems. These are the creamy-colored zones and the darker belts that give the planet a banded appearance. Astronomers think the zones are areas of high pressure, while the belts are low-pressure regions. The zones are the tops of the white clouds high in Jupiter's atmosphere. The belts are deeper parts of the atmosphere, 12 miles (20 km) below the zones, where sulfur and other minor elements in the atmosphere mix with hydrogen and ammonia to form yellow and brown gas clouds.

Because Jupiter's atmosphere is so deep, enormous pressures build up inside it. One theory is that the center of Jupiter is made of hydrogen under so much pressure that it becomes a liquid. Another theory is that the planet has a rocky core, not much larger than Earth. No one is certain, however. The Galileo spacecraft released a probe into Jupiter's atmosphere in December 1995, but this survived for only 57 minutes before being crushed by the enormous pressures.

The most spectacular feature of Jupiter's atmosphere is the Great Red Spot, which scientists think is a huge storm. The spot is twice the size of Earth, and it has been seen on and off for over 300 years. It changes color from one year to the next, and sometimes it even disappears completely, only to return later.

LOOK CLOSER

Jupiter's Moons

Jupiter's system of at least 16 moons is dominated by four: Io, Europa, Ganymede, and Callisto. They are often called Galilean satellites because they were first observed by Italian astronomer Galileo Galilei (1564–1642). Each is around the size of Earth's Moon and have their own distinct features.

Io is the smallest of the Galileans and the closest to Jupiter. Its interior (inside) is pulled around by the planet's colossal gravity, making Io the most volcanic world in the Solar System. Huge eruptions regularly spout sulfur across the moon's surface. In the low gravity, this sulfur can escape into space, forming a ring of sulfur along Io's orbit.

Europa is a completely different world, covered in a thick layer of ice. Astronomers think the ice protects a huge ocean of water, possibly home to alien life. There may be black smokers below the surface and vents supporting weird life-forms. Undersea volcanoes provide heat and nourishment for life on Earth and might do the same on Europa.

Ganymede is the largest Galilean satellite. It is 1.5 times the size of Earth's Moon. The Galileo space probe discovered that Ganymede has a magnetic field around it, so it may have a molten iron core similar to Earth's.

Callisto's surface is covered in brilliant craters, left over from the time when it formed. This moon is a mixture of rock and ice, which is darker and dirtier than Europa. Some astronomers think that Callisto may also have an ocean hidden beneath its crust.

CHECK THESE OUT!

✔ASTRONOMY ✔SOLAR SYSTEM ✔SPACE ✔SUN

Jurassic Period

Geologic time period when dinosaurs and their reptile relatives lived on Earth

HIGHLIGHTS 

- The Jurassic period began about 208 million years ago and ended 144 million years ago.
- The supercontinent of Pangaea began to break up during the Jurassic period with the opening of the Atlantic Ocean.

During the Jurassic period, between about 208 million and 144 million years ago, Earth was warmer and its climate less varied than today. There were no, or very small, ice caps at the poles and therefore the sea levels were higher than today with less land showing. Extensive shallow seas flooded over the continents forming islands, narrow seaways, and vast lagoons (shallow pools). Life flourished in the relatively warm and shallow waters.

Landmasses and movements

At the start of the Jurassic period, the continents were clustered together to form a supercontinent called Pangaea (pan-JEE-uh). A rising column of hot mantle rock domed up, stretching part of Pangaea so it began to rift apart. The upwelling hot rock broke through the thinned continental crust with outpouring of lavas (LAH-vuhz; molten or liquid rock). Huge amounts of dust and gas were thrown into the atmosphere. As the continents drifted apart, they took on the appearance of the modern world. North America drifted northward away from Africa and Eurasia as the Atlantic opened northward. An ancient ocean called the Tethys divided eastern Eurasia from the southern large continent of Gondwana.

By late Jurassic times, Gondwana began to break up into the separate continents of South America and Africa. Antarctica, India, and Australia, however, still clustered together in the Southern Hemisphere.

Life on land

The beginning of the Jurassic period was marked by a major extinction event when many species (types) of living organisms were wiped out. This event may have been caused by a rapid climate change and rising sea levels. It took some time for plant and animal life to recover, but by

This artwork shows a herd of gigantic titanosaurs crossing a river in Jurassic times.

LOOK CLOSER

The Rise of the Dinosaurs

Although the dinosaurs first evolved in earlier Triassic times, it was in the Jurassic period that they really came to dominate the world's landscapes. Some of the Jurassic dinosaurs became spectacularly large and included plant-eating giant sauropods such as Diplodocus (dip-LAHD-uh-kuhs) and Apatosaurus (ah-PAT-oh-SAWR-us). Some of these huge, four-legged beasts were over 90 feet (27 m) long and weighed around 33 tons (30 tonnes), much bigger than any land animal alive today or at any other time in Earth's history. Such large animals could survive only when there was plenty of plant food because they needed to eat enormous quantities of plants every day. Plant material is generally indigestible, so it took a long time to be processed in the animal's stomach. The larger the stomach the better, but that added weight and meant that plant-eating dinosaurs needed ever-larger supporting skeletons. However, their huge size protected them from predatory (hunting) carnivorous (meat-eating) dinosaurs such as Allosaurus, Megalosaurus, and Ceratosaurus. Allosaurus was a fearsome, two-legged giant with curved and jagged teeth. It grew to 40 feet (12 m) in length and had a skull 3 feet (1 m) long. However, because Allosaurus was so big, it could not have moved very fast and may have been an ambush predator or a scavenger that eats animals that have already been killed. Even a fully grown Allosaurus would not have taken on a giant sauropod, but it might have attacked a young or sickly one that had become separated from the herd.

Dinosaur footprints show that many of the plant eaters moved around in family groups or herds for safety, as large plant-eating mammals do today. The large predators, however, would have hunted alone. Small, fast-running dinosaur predators, such as Ornitholestes and Coelurus, may well have hunted in packs. Most scientist believe that the first birds evolved (developed) from a group of small, two-legged theropod dinosaurs. In recent years, small, feathered dinosaurs have been found in late Jurassic or early Cretaceous age rocks in China.

Allosaurus used its tail for balancing.

mid-Jurassic times, forests were flourishing again. Some of the old Paleozoic forest plants, the club mosses, ferns, and horsetails, were still around at this time. However, they were gradually replaced by plants more typical of the Mesozoic era of which the Jurassic was a part, such as ginkgos, conifers, and cycads (SY-KADZ). Plant fossils (remains or traces) show that global climates throughout most of the Jurassic were mild.

Dinosaurs and their reptile relatives evolved in different ways and filled most of the habitats on land, in the air, and in the sea. Modern amphibians such as the frogs evolved, and small, shrew-sized mammals became common.

Life in the seas

The shallow and warm Jurassic seas encouraged the growth of extensive coral and sponge reefs that provided food and shelter for other types of sea creatures and plants. Shoals of fish and small crustaceans (krus-TAY-shunz; shrimplike creatures) swarmed among thickets of sea lilies and algae (AL-jee; plantlike organisms) that grew attached to the reefs. Larger predatory bony fish, sharks, and ambush-hunting reptilian plesiosaurs lurked in the shadows. In the more open waters, the fast-swimming and hunting ichthyosaurs (IK-thee-uh-SAWRZ) chased shoals of squidlike cephalopods (SEF-uh-loh-PAHDZ), such as belemnites. The coiled ammonites (A-muh-NYTS) were mostly protected by their shells as they slowly swam around. Ammonites rapidly evolved into many different types, and their fossil shell remains are used by geologists to date Jurassic marine strata (STRAH-tuh; rock layers). Ammonites are the best-known Jurassic fossils.

CHECK THESE OUT!

✔CRETACEOUS PERIOD ✔GEOLOGIC TIMESCALE ✔PANGAEA ✔TRIASSIC PERIOD

Lake

A large area of fresh or salty water filling a hollow in Earth's surface

There are many bodies of inland (separated from the ocean) water, such as ponds, lakes, and inland seas. Lakes are larger than ponds but smaller than inland seas. Some are natural; others are artificial. Some are shallow; others are deep. Many lakes contain fresh water, but others are salty, although not as salty as inland seas. There are about 30,000 cubic miles (125,000 cu km) of freshwater lakes in the world, and about 25,000 cubic miles (104,000 cu km) of saltwater lakes.

On a map it is easy to see that there are many more lakes in some regions than in others. North America, especially Canada, has many lakes. South America has relatively few lakes, despite the continent's high rainfall.

In terms of area, the largest lake in the world is Lake Superior on the border between Canada and the United States. It has a surface area of 32,007 square miles (82,900 sq km). This freshwater lake is one of a string of connected lakes called the Great Lakes. Together, the Great Lakes make up 94,700 square miles (245,240 sq km) in area, and 6,000 cubic miles (25,000 cu km) in volume. Lake Baikal in Russia is the world's largest single body of freshwater, with a volume of 5,520 cubic miles (23,000 cu km). It is also the deepest lake.

Formation of lakes

Glaciers have been important in the formation of lakes, particularly in the northern temperate regions. During the Pleistocene era (a period in the Quaternary era, around 2 million to 10,000 years ago), large areas were covered with thick ice. As the glaciers grew, they moved slowly down valleys and gouged out huge amounts of rock. Then, as the ice age finished and the glaciers retreated, they left behind the rocky material as moraines (accumulations of earth and stones left by glaciers). As the ice melted, these moraines formed natural river dams that blocked the valleys and created lakes. The lakes are long and thin, following the contours of the valleys.

HIGHLIGHTS

- Lakes can be formed by ice age glaciers, movement of Earth's surface, volcanic activity, or by the blockage of river water.
- Around half of the world's lakes are freshwater.
- Humanmade lakes are constructed to provide drinking water or hydroelectric power.

The Great Lakes are (from left to right): Superior, Michigan, Huron, Erie, and Ontario.

Other types of glacial lakes include cirques (SUHRKS), bowl-shaped hollows on the sides of a mountain, and those caused as glaciers scoured pits in flat areas of hard rock. This action produced small lakes dotting the landscape, such as in large areas of Canada and Finland.

River systems can also produce lakes. As a lowland river flows across its floodplain, it often forms meanders (mee-AHN-duhrz; windings). When the river finds a shorter route downstream, a meander may get cut off. If there is sufficient water flowing into it from the plain, this cutoff section can form an oxbow lake. Flooding can also produce lakes in a floodplain.

When a river is held up on its way to the ocean by a barrier such as sand dunes, a lake can develop very close to the sea. This lake is called a coastal lagoon. Its water may be fresh, brackish (a little salty), or salty. The levels of water can vary with the state of the tide or with changes in the flow of river water entering the lagoon.

Lakes can also be formed by changes in Earth's surface. Very large lakes can result from faults (breaks) in Earth's crust, as in rift valleys. There are two great series of rift valleys in Africa: the western and eastern rifts. The western rift system contains Lake Tanganyika and Lake Nyasa farther south. The eastern rift includes the lakes of Tanzania and Kenya, lakes in Ethiopia, and the Sea of Galilee in northeast Israel.

Where the land has slipped downward between faults, a graben (GRAH-buhn) lake is formed. Lake Tahoe is a good example. Volcanic activity can result in lakes. Crater lakes are formed when an old volcanic crater fills with water, for example, Crater Lake in Oregon.

Salt lakes form where the evaporation is high and the flow of water is not enough to carry the salt away. Great Salt Lake in Utah is an example. Many of the lakes of the East African rift are not salty but contain strong solutions of sodium carbonate from nearby volcanic soils.

Lakes and human life

People have long used lakes as a way of irrigating (watering) crops and as sources of drinking water and food. Lakes have become more vulnerable to pollution, due to human sewage and more intense methods of farming. High nitrogen levels can upset the ecological balance, with serious consequences for wildlife.

Taking too much water from a lake can also create problems. The level of Lake Baikal is falling, for example, because irrigation systems take away more water than flows into the lake.

Artificial lakes have been created to make reservoirs for drinking water or as a source of hydroelectric power. Building dams to flood valleys has also made it possible to control river flow downstream and so avoid the seasonal flooding of lower areas.

CHECK THESE OUT!
✔HYDROLOGY ✔INLAND SEA ✔RIVER

Lakes are completely surrounded by land, such as this one on Fraser Island in Australia.

Landform

Distinctive topographic feature on Earth's surface

The surface features that make Earth so varied are called landforms. They range in size from a valley such as the Grand Canyon to caves and sea stacks, deltas, plateaus (pla-TOHZ; raised plains), moraines (muh-RAYNZ; soil and stone deposits), and even small sand ripples on the shore. The science that studies how these features are formed is called geomorphology (JEE-uh-mawr-FAHL-uh-jee).

Landforms are placed in groups according to how they were made. Some are tectonic (tek-TAH-nik), formed by movements in Earth's crust. Others are denudational (dee-nyoo-DAY-shuhn-uhl), made by erosion and weathering processes. The final group are depositional landforms, formed when rivers and glaciers heap up masses of sediment. Humans have created such large features, such as reservoirs, quarries, and canals, that some scientists feel there should be a category called humanmade landforms.

Because of the action of weathering and erosion, landforms are constantly changing. The present shape of any landform will reflect the climate of the area and the rock type and structure. If time allows, any part of Earth's surface may eventually become flat due to erosion and weathering. Usually, however, often because of plate tectonics and Earth's crustal movements, new mountain ranges form high above sea level.

HIGHLIGHTS

- The distinctive features on Earth's surface are called landforms.
- The types of rocks in an area influence the types of landforms that are created there.

History of ideas

Before the 18th century, people thought Earth had been created as a perfect place and was gradually decaying. Scottish geologist James Hutton (1726–1797) believed that Earth was very old and that its surface had changed many times. In 1899, U.S. geologist William Morris Davis (1850–1934) suggested that landforms developed in a cycle, passing through stages that he called youth, maturity, and old age. In the youthful stage, a newly uplifted area would be actively eroded with deep, V-shaped valleys. During maturity, the landscape would be less steep and erosion would not be as active. In old age, the rivers would flow slowly over a flat plain.

In the 1950s and 1960s, the importance of climate in shaping landforms was realized. The theory of plate tectonics showed that areas of Earth's crust move to create new surface features.

Tectonic landforms

Large-scale movement of Earth's crust can create mountains or vast low-lying areas. The theory of plate tectonics explains that Earth's outer shell is made of a number of hard plates in constant slow motion. Volcanic activity, large-scale faulting, and other events are concentrated where the plates meet. The African Rift

The state of Utah has a number of canyons. These are formed through erosion by wind and water.

valley is a large-scale landform caused by faulting in Earth's crust. Here, two parallel faults have caused the land between them to sink, making the rift valley. The Andes mountains in South America were formed where an ocean plate, forming the floor of the Pacific, has been pushed beneath the South American continent.

Denudational landforms

Denudation includes all the processes of erosion and weathering that act on Earth's surface and wear it down. These forces include: fluvial (FLOO-vee-uhl; river processes), glacial (ice processes), coastal, and eolian (ee-OH-lee-uhn; wind action, mainly in desert areas) forces. Groundwater (water that lies underground within rocks) can also cause erosion, as can gravity when mud slides and rock falls occur. Climate also strongly influences the type of denudation that is active in any place. River systems will occur mainly in areas of high rainfall and moderate temperatures, and glacial conditions will occur at high latitude and high altitude. Some rocks are more easily broken down than others, and a hard layer of rock may lead to the formation of a waterfall in a river valley.

Rivers shape the landscape by cutting V-shaped valleys and by transporting eroded material away. This sediment (SEH-duh-muhnt), made of anything from boulders and pebbles to sand grains and mud, may eventually be deposited in the sea. River valleys form a network called a drainage basin, which seen from above may resemble the branches of a tree. Usually there will be a main river, and the branches are the tributary (TRIH-byuh-ter-ee) streams. Glaciers are less flexible than rivers. They grind across the bedrock, producing deep U-shaped valleys and high mountain corries.

The coastline is shaped by the waves, sea currents, and water running down cliff faces. Stacks, arches, and caves are erosional features. In many deserts, rock pedestals have grooved bases where wind-blown sand has cut into them.

Depositional landforms

Eroded sediment is carried by a river or glacier to be deposited as a new landform elsewhere. River sediment makes deltas and levees, while glacial material is heaped up in moraines. On the coast, sand is deposited as bars and beaches, and wind forms dunes (DOONZ) in desert regions.

These depositional landforms may in time become new layers of sedimentary rock. Locked in their structure and grains are the clues to how they were made. Pebbles deposited by a river or by the sea on a beach, for example, are often rounded, whereas the rock fragments eroded by glaciers are jagged and angular.

LOOK CLOSER

Coral Reefs

Living organisms have built some amazing landforms. Off the northeast coast of Australia, the Great Barrier Reef (shown below) has been built by tiny animals called coral polyps (PAH-luhps). In the Pacific Ocean, there are many coral islands made in a similar way. The Great Barrier Reef is over 1,250 miles (2,000 km) long and covers 80,000 square miles (207,000 sq km). It has been growing for over 25 million years. The polyps look similar to small sea anemones. Each polyp builds a small amount of coral, which in time makes a huge mass of limestone. As the sea bed slowly sinks, the corals keep on building so the living ones are just below sea level. Coral reefs are excellent places for creatures to live. There is plenty of food and shelter for fish, sponges, and many other organisms. However, coral reefs are threatened by human activities.

CHECK THESE OUT!

✔CANYON ✔CAVE ✔CLIFF ✔COAST
✔CRATER ✔DELTA ✔DESERT ✔EROSION ✔GLACIER
✔GROUNDWATER ✔MOUNTAIN ✔RIVER ✔VALLEY

Laser

Device that produces coherent beams of light or other radiation

A laser is a source of brilliant light of one color, used in a variety of applications. The word *laser* stands for Light Amplification and Stimulated Emission of Radiation. A laser is different from any other type of light because it is monochromatic (MAHN-uh-kroh-MAT-ik; pure light of just one color) and because it is coherent (koh-HIR-uhnt). Coherent light waves travel in step with each other. They are very strong and intense.

Normal light is a mixture of different colors. Each color has a different wavelength (the length of a light wave between one peak and the next, as in a water wave). Most sources of light release millions of waves every second, each in a tiny packet called a photon (FOH-tahn). Even if two photons have the same color and wavelength, they are unlikely to be produced with the precise timing that makes them coherent.

HIGHLIGHTS

- Lasers produce light that is monochromatic (all of one color and wavelength) and coherent (all the waves are in phase with each other).
- Laser light is made by stimulated emission—using one photon of light to trigger an atom to release a second, identical photon.
- Lasers have applications ranging from surgery to telecommunications, and from industry to basic research.

How a laser works

Lasers produce coherent light from atoms by a method called stimulated emission. All light comes from atoms. When an atom absorbs energy, the electrons inside it can change their orbits around the central nucleus (NOO-klee-uhs). This process gives the atom more energy. The atom becomes excited. However, this higher energy level is always somewhat unstable. The electrons quickly drop back to their normal positions and release energy as photons of light. The more energy released by an atom, the shorter the wavelength of light it makes. The structure of atoms and molecules (groups of atoms) means that the electrons inside them can only jump between certain energy levels, so they can only release certain wavelengths and colors of light.

The photograph below shows an infrared laser cutting through a plate of steel. This is a test to see if the laser can be used in the car industry.

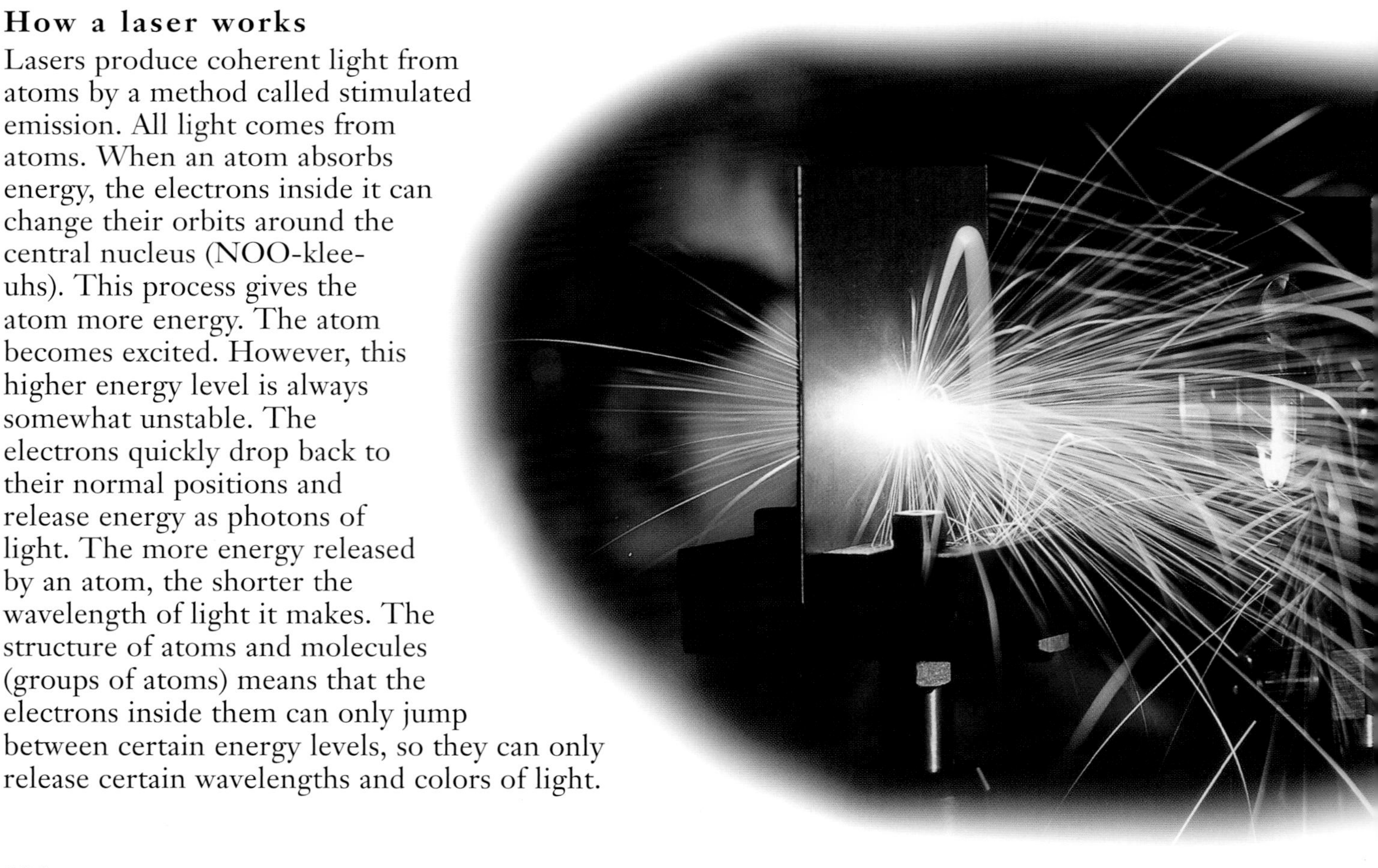

The electrons in an excited atom usually drop back to their normal energy level at random, so the process is called spontaneous emission. However, if a photon of the right wavelength is passing by the atom, its effect on the electrons is such that the atom is likely to emit a photon exactly in step with the first. This process is called stimulated emission.

A laser uses stimulated emission to produce a cascade (series) of coherent photons. Each emission produces two identical photons where only one had existed previously. These photons eventually build up into an intense beam of laser light. Producing a laser beam needs special materials, however.

Stimulated emission is impossible in most substances. This is because the atoms usually do not stay excited for long enough to be hit by a passing photon. However, a few materials called lasing mediums have atoms or molecules that remain in a metastable (MET-uh-STAY-buhl) excited state for much longer than usual—sometimes up to several thousandths of a second. Using a lasing medium makes it much more probable that stimulated emission will happen.

LOOK CLOSER

Masers

Lasers do not have to produce visible light. Lasers that produce microwave radiation are called masers. Because microwaves carry less energy than visible light, masers are easier to build. They were invented before lasers. The first masers used gases whose atoms were excited by a strong electric field. More modern designs use crystals such as ruby. Both types are tunable—they can produce a number of different wavelengths of maser, depending on the setup of the system.

Masers are widely used as amplifiers for weak radio and electrical signals. For example, they are used to magnify weak radio signals from deep space picked up by radio telescopes. Masers are also used in electronic circuits to filter out the noise caused by the atoms inside the circuit moving around as the circuit heats up. In both cases, the noise that interferes with the important signal will have random scattered wavelengths. However, because the maser can be tuned to multiply only the exact wavelength of the important signal, it is able to filter out nearly all of the unwanted noise.

Building a laser

The way in which a laser is built depends very much on the lasing medium it uses. Laboratory lasers, which produce the most powerful laser beams, use gas or a liquid laser dye inside a tube with reflective walls. In a gas laser, an electric current excites the lasing medium into its metastable state.

The first atom that spontaneously emits a photon will trigger a cascade of stimulated emissions. Because the sides of the tube are reflective, they will bounce back any photons that hit them. The only photons able to travel any distance will be the ones moving in parallel (straight) paths along the length of the tube. The ends of the tube are mirrored so that they mostly reflect back and multiply the strength of the beam. To produce a continuous laser beam, one end of the mirror is made semi-silvered so that some light can escape. Short pulses of light can be made by fitting the tube with a shutter that opens and closes.

A liquid dye laser works by the same principle, but the molecules in the lasing medium are excited by a brilliant light source. Some laser dyes have more than one metastable state, so they can produce laser beams of different wavelengths. The wavelength is selected by firing light of the right color into the dye to trigger the cascade of emissions.

The most common types of laser are solid-state lasers. These are both stronger and cheaper than powerful dye and gas lasers. Rubies and other crystals are used inside laser pointers and other cheap devices. In electronics, semiconductor lasers are used. These lasers produce a cone of laser light at the junction

STORY OF SCIENCE

Star Wars

One of the most ambitious plans for lasers was the Star Wars program or the Strategic Defense Initiative (SDI). Star Wars was developed by U.S. scientists and politicians from the early 1980s onward, when the United States was still locked in the Cold War confrontation with the Soviet Union. The idea of SDI was to create a network of lasers in space above Earth. In the event of a war, these lasers would be able to destroy nuclear missiles high in the atmosphere before they got close to the United States or its allies.

SDI would have needed very powerful lasers to shoot down missiles hundreds of miles away. One idea was to use huge chemical lasers, each about the size of a railroad car, whose laser beams would have been aimed at missiles using a movable mirror and radar. Another idea used a small nuclear explosion to generate lasers from crystal rods aimed at the target.

With the end of the Cold War and the collapse of the Soviet Union, SDI was scrapped. Most scientists thought it would be impossible to overcome the practical problems anyway. Some said the lasers would lose their power as they passed through the atmosphere. Others thought that if the enemy gave their missiles a reflective shell, most of the laser energy could be reflected harmlessly.

This artist's impression of SDI shows a laser being fired at a target satellite from a shuttle.

between two different types of semiconductor material. Semiconductor lasers are most commonly used in CD players.

Uses of lasers

Lasers have a huge range of uses. Many rely on their intensity as a source of heat and light. Others make use of the fact that they produce coherent light of one precise wavelength. Applications that rely on a laser's intensity include medicine and manufacturing. Laser surgery is common today. A laser beam can be focused to form a cutting tool much sharper than the sharpest scalpel. It has the advantage that its heat seals the wound afterward. Laser cutters are also used for cutting through steel and other materials in manufacturing. The line they cut can be much more tightly controlled than an electric arc or any other cutting tool. Laser beams can also be focused through the transparent lens of the eye to perform delicate surgery on the retina.

As laser beams keep their intensity over very long distances, they are also useful for sending information. Fiber-optic cables carry pulses of laser light that bounce from side to side within the optical fiber and emerge just as intense at the other end.

Light-sensitive detectors can also be set to detect a single wavelength of light produced by a laser. Devices such as CD players and barcode readers are able to detect changes to a laser beam bounced off a reflective surface. Once detected, they change these into electronic signals. Laser tape measures record the time a laser takes to bounce off a distant object and be reflected back. Because the laser always travels at the speed of light, the measure can work out the precise distance to the object.

Lasers are also used as coherent sources of light for making holograms. A hologram is a three-dimensional image that is a record of the interference between two light beams traveling along different paths. Because the light waves in both beams have to be in step with each other at the start, a laser is the ideal source of light for this application.

CHECK THESE OUT!

✔ATOM ✔ELECTRON ✔HOLOGRAPHY ✔LIGHT

Glossary

amphibians (am-FIH-bee-uhnz) Cold-blooded animals adapted to live both on land and in the water, such as frogs, toads, newts, and salamanders.

aquifer (A-kwuh-fuhr) Water-bearing layer of rock.

atoll (A-tawl) Roughly ring-shaped coral island.

broadcast To transmit sound or images by radio or television.

Cold War Period of hostile relations between the Soviet Union (USSR) and the United States that never escalated into open war; lasted from 1945 until 1991.

eclipse (ih-KLIPS) When one celestial body obscures another.

eddy (EH-dee) Current of water or air that runs against the general flow.

floodplain Level land that becomes flooded when a river bursts its banks.

food chain The order of organisms in a community, whereby each depends on another as its food source.

galvanize (GAL-vuh-nyz) To coat with zinc.

gyroscope (JY-ruh-SKOHP) Wheel or disk with a rod through its center, mounted so that the wheel spins freely.

hot spot Point where molten rock inside Earth melts through the crust, forming volcanic features.

interglacial period Period when most of Earth's surface is free of year-round ice.

kinetic energy Energy of movement.

landfill Hole dug in the earth, filled with waste and covered.

landlocked With no outlet to the ocean.

lens Piece of transparent material used to focus rays of light.

midlatitudes Temperate regions between 30 and 60 degrees north and south of the equator.

moraines (muh-RAYNZ) Clusters of earth and stones carried and deposited by a glacier.

nuclear reactor Device for the controlled release of nuclear energy.

polarization of light Affecting light waves so that they vibrate in a particular pattern.

prairies (PREHR-eez) Large areas of flattish grassland.

radiotherapy Medical treatment that uses radiation, such as X rays.

runoff Rain or meltwater that runs into a body of water.

saturation Being filled completely with another substance to the point where no more can be taken in.

seeding clouds Dropping silver iodide crystals into clouds from an airplane in order to make the clouds rain.

sewage (SOO-ij) Waste liquids or matter carried off in disposal pipes and tunnels called sewers.

sill Underwater ridge separating the beds of two deeper bodies of water.

solvent Substance (usually liquid), which dissolves a solid to form a solution.

strait Narrow passage of water connecting two larger bodies of water.

striated (STRY-AY-tuhd) Striped.

sublimation (SUH-bluh-MAY-shun) When a solid changes into a gas without passing through a liquid state first.

submersible (sub-MUHR-suh-buhl) Vehicle that is designed and built to operate under water.

terrestrial planets The rocky planets of the inner Solar System. They are Mercury, Venus, Earth, and Mars.

urban Coming from or involving the city as opposed to the countryside.

Index

Page numbers in **boldface type** refer to main articles and their illustrations. Page numbers in *italic type* refer to additional illustrations.

05/06	DATE DUE		

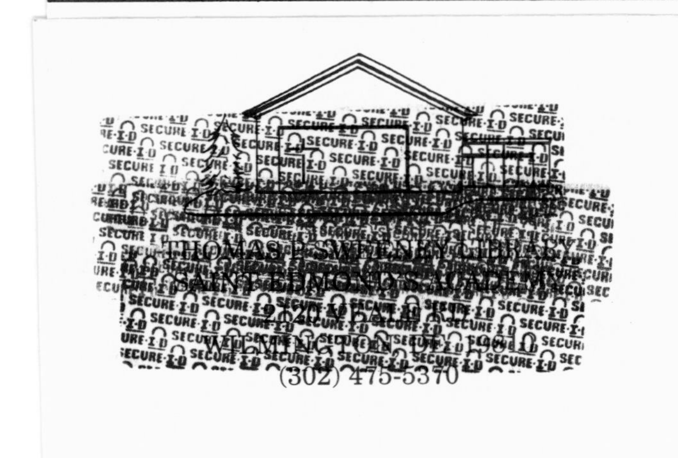